*Turning on Water
with a Shovel*

Elwood Mead, Commissioner of the Bureau of Reclamation
April 1924 to January 1936
(Wyoming State Museum)

Turning on

WATER

with a

SHOVEL

The Career of Elwood Mead

JAMES R. KLUGER

University of New Mexico Press

Albuquerque

Library of Congress Cataloging in Publication Data
Kluger, James R.
Turning on water with a shovel : the career of Elwood Mead /
James R. Kluger. — 1st ed.
p. cm.
Includes bibliographical references and index.
ISBN 0-8263-1382-5 (cl) : $29.95
1. Mead, Elwood, 1858–1936. 2. Irrigation engineers—West
(U.S.)—Biography. 3. Irrigation engineering—West (U.S.)—
History. 4. Water reuse—West (U.S.)—History. I. Title.
TC928.2.M43K58 1992
627'.5'092—dc20
[B]   92-8337
CIP

FOR
The unknown soul who made this possible
And for all those who have given the gift of life
And allowed dreams to come true

Contents

Illustrations following page 40

Foreword

ELWOOD MEAD WAS A MAN OF VISION AND IDEAL-
ism. His career stretched from the 1880s into the 1930s, crucial
decades in the development of urban-industrial America and the
arid and semiarid American West. Like many of his contempo-
raries, he saw the settlement of the West as an antidote to conges-
tion in eastern cities and to the boom-and-bust economy of the
nineteenth century West, an economy which had been based
largely on mining and grazing. By the 1890s, many social critics
assumed that industrialization would inexorably replace factory
workers with machines, limit wages, and shrink economic opportunity. The depression of 1893–1898—the worst in American history save for the Great Depression of the 1930s—reinforced that
conviction. Simultaneously, the "disappearing West" became a
powerful theme in art, literature, and popular culture, and a vigorous back-to-nature or back-to-the-land movement reflected the
assumption that urban middle-class life had become too soft and
over-refined.

In the dying decades of the nineteenth and opening decades of
the twentieth century, many engineers considered themselves social planners and arbiters of material progress. They recognized
that industrialization had created new social and economic problems, but it also spawned technological innovations that ostensibly

gave human beings increasing power over nature. At the same time, several social and intellectual currents converged to give the family farm an even more powerful emotional appeal than it had traditionally enjoyed. The agrarian myth had long been the lodestone of the American value system. At its heart was the assumption that life close to the soil was more natural and virtuous than an urban existence. The small farm not only strengthened individualism, it also fortified the family and shored up republican institutions. Those who owned property took their civic responsibilities more seriously, and they had the economic independence to act on their convictions—in contrast to factory workers, who were assumed to feel less social responsibility and whose votes were more easily manipulated.

All these ideas were "in the air" during Mead's fifty year career as an irrigation engineer, but his affection for the family farm came from bitter personal experience. He grew up on an Indiana farm in the Ohio Valley, about forty miles south of Cincinnati. He was seven-years-old at the end of the Civil War, and by that time land speculators had already begun to acquire farms in his neighborhood. The land was subsequently leased to tenants who had fled Tennessee and Kentucky during the war. The newcomers did little to preserve the fertility of the soil or to support the schools and churches so necessary to the life of proud and prosperous towns and villages. No better example of the causal link between landownership and civic virtue could have been provided. This experience also convinced Mead that rural life had become dreary, stifling, and unappealing, and that something had to be done to make it more attractive.

Mead first went West in the 1880s, after he graduated from college. He began his career as an irrigation engineer in Colorado, but did not reach national prominence until the 1890s, when he became the new state of Wyoming's first state engineer. Like most western states and territories, Wyoming had been hit hard by the depression of the 1890s and desperately needed to attract new set-

tlers and outside capital. Mead believed that the federal government was unlikely to build irrigation works, and if it did states like
Wyoming would inevitably lose out to those with much larger
populations—particularly California and Colorado—in the annual battles for appropriations. Moreover, while the central government controlled the public lands, the states exercised administrative supervision over the allocation of water; some way had to
be found to unify authority over the two resources. Mead also
realized that in the Rocky Mountain West, no plan to encourage
irrigation could win support in the legislature unless it combined
farming and stock-raising. Since most of Wyoming was public
land not subject to state taxes, since Wyoming had great trouble
paying the costs of government during the 1890s, and since range
wars became increasingly common during that decade, Mead became the architect of various plans to cede all or part of the arid
lands to the states. Because Wyoming's leaders feared that the state
could not survive with such a small population and tax base, one
of the West's most thinly populated regions provided most of the
important land and water legislation introduced in Congress at the
end of the last century.

With the help of his patron, Wyoming's powerful U.S. Senator
Francis E. Warren, Mead won control of a new Office of Irrigation Inquiry created within the Department of Agriculture in 1898.
From this new power base, he tried but failed to secure control of
the federal reclamation program launched by the Interior Department in 1902. Subsequently, he became a bitter critic of the policies followed by the Reclamation Service, but at this time his
views of the nation's responsibility to conduct social planning
were inconsistent. On the one hand, he feared that making irrigation a national responsibility would threaten state control over
water; on the other, he thought that Washington had the obligation to take the lead in planning and directing settlement of the
rural West. On any number of occasions, Mead could have left
government for much more lucrative jobs as a consultant, but he

was imbued with a deep sense of public responsibility. In 1907, he moved to Australia to help the Victorian government lay out model rural communities, or "closer settlements" as Mead termed them. Victoria's leaders had the same goal as politicians in the American West: to use irrigation to attract new settlers and promote economic growth. Australia, however, was not afraid to use the power of the state to encourage the common good. Mead considered the years spent "down under" as proof that, under the right circumstances, his dreams could be realized.

By 1915, when Mead returned to the United States, he was an international figure, and he subsequently drafted rural development plans for Hawaii and Palestine. Unfortunately, in the United States his planning attempts were largely unsuccessful. During the 1920s, low crop prices, the lure of urban life, and a renewed antipathy toward government paternalism made Mead's work difficult. His effort to create model agricultural colonies in California during World War I collapsed when land and crop prices plummeted in the early 1920s. And when he finally assumed the job of Commissioner of Reclamation in 1924, and heroically tried to broaden the Reclamation Bureau's vision and imagination, he met resistance from both Congress and the farmers he served. He died in 1936, at a time when New Deal planners were addressing the social problems that had preoccupied Mead for much of his life.

This is a biography long overdue. While John Wesley Powell has attracted many biographers, such important figures in western history as George H. Maxwell, Frederick Haynes Newell, William Ellsworth Smythe, and Elwood Mead have not received the attention they deserve, despite their efforts to build a "new West." Professor Kluger has done an admirable job of sketching Mead's career. His biography is thoroughly researched and written with clarity, precision, and a dedication few students of water in the West can match. The allocation and distribution of water is a complicated subject. General readers will applaud Professor Kluger for not getting bogged down in detail and for compressing a long story into a book of manageable length. This is a story over two decades in the making, one that has taken Professor Kluger all over the world in search of Elwood Mead. Every student of western history will profit from his efforts.

Donald J. Pisani
Merrick Professor of History
University of Oklahoma

Preface

EVERY BOOK HAS A STORY; THIS ONE'S TALE IS a near-quarter century odyssey. It began back in the late 1960s when Harwood Hinton, my mentor at the University of Arizona, suggested Elwood Mead as a topic for my dissertation. In those turbulent times, the historical profession was caught up in the hot topics of the day—war, race, and rebellion. Few scholars seemed interested in such mundane things as reclamation. Only a few hearty souls—most notably Larry Lee and Norris Hundley— were working in western waters. At first I was hesitant, but preliminary investigation changed my tepidness to enthusiasm as the dimensions and accomplishments of Mead's life unfolded.

As I began gathering materials, I quickly came to understand the logistical problems of research in reclamation. Sources are scattered all over the country—and in the case of Mead all over the world. I began a transcontinental research trek the day after man first landed on the moon. From Berkeley to Boston, with intermittent stops in Washington, D.C., Indiana, Iowa, Wyoming, Nevada, and Colorado, I gathered materials and visited the landmarks of Mead's past, stopping periodically to partake of the contemporary events of the times. With dissertation done, my plan was to get a job and revise the manuscript for publication.

Unfortunately, the completion of my doctorate coincided with the sudden evaporation of history positions in higher education. A one-year stint at the University of Utah was followed by four years at Texas College, a predominately black school in Tyler, Texas. Mead went on the back burner as the demands of beginning a teaching career and a heavy teaching load consumed my time and energies.

Fortunately, at Texas College I met a remarkable woman, Sister Francis de Chantal McLeese, a retired nun who came to teach chemistry at the same time I showed up. We became friends and, for the next twenty years, she was to be like the refrain of a ballad: "Get the book done! Get the book done," she goaded me every time we corresponded.

My next stop—seemingly now my last—brought me back to Tucson and to Pima College, where fortune smiled again. Community colleges offer little support or encouragement for research and publication. However, in 1978, a grant from the Myrtle L. Atkinson Foundation of California allowed me to visit Australia and Israel to do further research on Mead. Subsequent Atkinson Foundation grants in 1982 and 1986 made it possible for me to collect the rest of the material for this book.

Meanwhile, I tried to revise the manuscript during summer breaks, but made little progress. Finally, in 1988 I got a sabbatical and planned a swift completion of the book—only to be felled by kidney failure. The next year it seemed like I spent all my time either in doctor's offices or on dialysis. But fortune was to smile once more and on September 28, 1989, I received the gift of life—a new kidney. Recovery was remarkable and, with the rest of the semester off, I was able, at last, to finish the book. Harwood Hinton agreed to read the manuscript one more time, and by the fall of 1990, it was off to the University of New Mexico Press for evaluation and, later, acceptance.

So now, two decades later, the dissertation is at last seeing printer's ink. It is a changed world, and not just internationally. Where once only a few historians braved the irrigated fields of western water, today it is a popular and expanding field. New names—Pisani, Reisner, and Worster, to cite three—enliven and enhance the exploration and debate over reclamation in the West. Linked as it is to environmental issues and recent droughts, water has become a major contemporary concern and a hot topic for historians.

As people today seek to understand and explain the problems in arid America, they look back to the roots of such developments, and any examination of those origins will involve Elwood Mead. For over a half-century, his ideas and efforts intersected with the rise of irrigation in the American West. From the crude ditches he first encountered along the Cache le Poudre River in the 1880s to the construction of the giant dam in Boulder Canyon, his life parallelled the evolution of reclamation as a force in the modern world.

Over the many years that this book has been in the making, I have incurred numerous debts. I am torn between a blanket thanks and a detailed list of acknowledgments that inevitably would omit some key person. At the risk of offending, I wish to make a few specific citations. Harwood Hinton took over the direction of my program at a critical juncture, steered my doctorate to completion, and has been a tried, true, and trusted friend for over twenty years. Virginia Hutchison was instrumental in arranging the grants that enabled me to complete the research, and to her I extend my affectionate gratitude. David Holtby and the staff at the University of New Mexico Press have been exemplary in their assistance and support. Finally, to the many friends who have sustained me through the good times and the bad these last four years, I want to express my undying love.

*Turning on Water
with a Shovel*

ONE

The Early Years

ON FEBRUARY 14, 1936, SECRETARY OF THE IN-
terior Harold L. Ickes announced that the reservoir forming behind the recently completed Boulder Dam on the Colorado River
would be known as Lake Mead in honor of Elwood Mead, the
Commissioner of Reclamation who had died ten days earlier. It
was a fitting tribute to Mead that the then-largest artificial lake in
the world should perpetuate the name of this man who had devoted his life to the development of dry domains all over the globe.
For over fifty years, Mead had concerned himself with the problems of irrigation and irrigators, and the capstone of his remarkable career had been directing the construction of the behemoth
concrete wall that created the one-hundred-and-fifteen-mile-long
reservoir. Lake Mead was a monument to this preeminent cham-
pion of the conquest of arid America.

Elwood Mead's ancestral history is clearly rooted in America's
past. He was born on January 16, 1858, on the Indiana farm of his
parents, twenty-three-year-old Daniel B. and eighteen-year-old
Lucinda Davis Mead. The Meads traced their ancestry back to
John Mead, who came from England to Greenwich, Connecticut,
about 1737. The family lived in Vermont for a few years and then
moved to Westchester County, New York, where James Mead,
Elwood's grandfather, was born in the early 1800s. James tried his

hand at architecture in New York City for a while, but grew restless, and like thousands of others during this period, set out with
his family for the promised land to the west. The flow of immigrants through the Cumberland Gap, begun as a trickle at the time
of the American Revolution, was at floodtide by the War of 1812,
when the Mead family entered the upper Ohio Valley. Their travels ended about forty miles below Cincinnati, on what is known
as the East Bend of the Ohio River, three miles north of Patriot,
Indiana. There, James purchased a small farm on a bluff overlooking the river.[1]

Nineteenth-century America was predominately a land of farmers, and Switzerland County, where the Meads settled, was exclu-
sively agrarian. The southern half of the county was populated
with Swiss, from whence came its name, and the northern part by
English and Scotch-Irish. The Mead family did well and acquired
substantial holdings, eventually owning over nine hundred acres.
The land sat high on steep hills, however, and much of its rich soil
eventually eroded to the river. Nevertheless, the Meads enjoyed a
comfortable living and built a substantial home overlooking the
Ohio. The house contained James's extensive book collection,
which local residents boasted was the largest personal library in
the state.[2]

Elwood's maternal grandparents lived across the river, in Kentucky. Their ancestry was more obscure than the Meads'. His
grandfather, Thomas Davis, was an orphan, who had been
brought to Kentucky as a young boy by an uncle from his home
near Mount Vernon, Virginia. Family legend has it that the Davis
family had been wealthy, but that young Davis inherited no
money. A slave who looked after the lad and accompanied him to
Kentucky disappeared; some claimed the uncle sold him because
he knew too much. Nonetheless, Davis had become a moderately
successful slave-owning farmer in Boone County by the time his
daughter Lucinda married Daniel Mead in 1857.[3]

After the wedding, the young couple moved to a farm carved

from James Mead's holdings. Elwood was their first child, followed by Emily a year and a half later. In the ensuing years, these two children were joined by brothers James and Scott, and sisters Emma, Edna, and Grace. The farm did well; the family grew tobacco and corn, and raised sheep and a few cattle. The Civil War largely passed them by since Daniel was not called to arms. Their only "contact" with the conflict came during a foray of Morgan's Raiders into southeastern Indiana in the summer of 1863. Lucinda was at home alone when word came that the Confederates were approaching. She took the children and hid, in a hillside cave at the base of a huge oak tree, until the supposed danger had passed. Life on the farm soon returned to normal.[4]

By the time the Civil War ended, Elwood was seven years old and had begun his integration into farm life. Gradually, he assumed more chores, but his duties were heaviest during the planting and harvest seasons when his father hired ex-slaves for fifty cents a day to supplement the family efforts. Young Mead's life was not all drudgery. He read extensively from his grandfather's library, and spent long summer days playing in the groves of oak, ash, wild cherry, hickory, poplar, and walnut trees along the slopes of the Ohio River. But this idyllic life was marred by a wanton wastefulness that Mead would lament in later life. He saw the beautiful trees disappear "like mists before the morning sun," as farmers cleared the land to grow corn and tobacco. As these crops had no binding material in their roots, the winter rains soon washed away the fertile surface soil. Elwood himself contributed to this ruthless destruction, splitting wild cherry trees to make fences. At the time, no one regretted this waste; as the natural resources were depleted, everyone under forty expected to move farther west and share in the bountiful land there.[5]

Perhaps even more damaging to Elwood's community was a demographic shift that took place while he was still a youth. Where all the nearby farmers once owned and worked their land, many gradually sold out to speculators who leased the properties to tenants. Most of the newcomers were Civil War "refugees" from the mountains of Tennessee and Kentucky. The renters not only ruined the soil by exploitive practices, but also broke down the community spirit that had prevailed. They took no interest in local affairs, went to church rarely if at all, and cared little about their children's education. On the other hand, they undoubtedly were looked down upon as outsiders and made to feel like intruders in the area. The sons of these tenants talked mainly of hunting, fighting, or chasing girls. Elwood, who had inherited a love of the soil from his father and a love of books from his grandfather, found that he had little in common with the neighboring boys. The social atmosphere of rural life stifled him. He planned to go to college not so much because of the lure beyond as because it was "the surest road" away from a life he had come to dislike.[6]

Elwood's earliest ambition had been to attend the U.S. Military Academy. After he completed his studies at the township school, Mead taught for one term and continued farming while he awaited word on his application to West Point. In 1877 he was accepted at "the Point" and entered the school in the fall. He stayed only a few weeks, however, for an illness, diagnosed as malaria, forced him to return home. The following fall he entered four-year-old Purdue University at Lafayette, Indiana.[7]

Elwood worked his way through college. At the age of fourteen, he had been employed as a rodman for county surveyors, and in subsequent summers, until his graduation, he worked as a surveyor. Annual expenses at Purdue were 169 dollars, but the state legislature provided four-year scholarships to two superior students from each county. These awards carried exemption from entrance, incidental, and room, heat, and light fees. An outstanding scholar from Switzerland County, Elwood received a thirty-three-dollar-a-year reduction. The university also hired students at ten cents an hour, and he obtained employment as a janitor in the evenings. This job left little time to study at night, so he developed the habit of rising early in the morning and doing his assignments before classes began.[8]

When Mead first arrived at Purdue, the fraternity men regarded him as something of a country bumpkin. He came from such a remote part of the state, and they quickly noted that he slept in the same shirt he wore to class. Although he had no interest in joining the Greek societies, he soon showed them that he was no "Hoosier hick." Elwood had read extensively in his grandfather's library, and that, together with an extraordinarily facile mind, more than compensated for any inferiority in his country-school education. Moreover, his magnetic personality quickly endeared him to his fellow students, and he easily proved himself in the classroom.[9]

The faculty likewise recognized the talents of the young scholar from Switzerland County. Professor Harvey W. Wiley, who later gained national fame in connection with pure food legislation, encouraged Mead to work with him in chemistry, but Elwood's interests were elsewhere. Instead, he studied under Dr. Charles Lee Ingersoll, who had been brought to Purdue in 1879 by President Emerson E. White to upgrade the School of Agriculture. White wanted a closer link between the classroom and the farm—the theoretical and the practical. Ingersoll's job was to conduct experimental work and to establish a model farm. Elwood's senior thesis demonstrated the ideal the president sought. Writing about tobacco, he combined the experiences of his father's farm with the knowledge gained at Purdue. At his graduation in June of 1882, Mead was granted a diploma bearing mention of special work in agriculture and science.[10]

After graduation, Mead was employed for seven months by the Army Engineer Corps as an assistant engineer in the survey and improvement of the Wabash River. He lived in Indianapolis, but spent most of his weekends in Lafayette, where he was courting Florence S. Chase, the daughter of a locally prominent lawyer and banker, Hiram W. Chase. After a December 20, 1882, wedding, the couple spent their honeymoon traveling to Fort Collins, in northern Colorado. His former mentor at Purdue, Dr. Ingersoll, had become president of Colorado State Agricultural College there in the fall of 1882, and Ingersoll had persuaded the young Hoosier to join the faculty as professor of mathematics and physics.[11]

When he arrived in Fort Collins, Mead found the situation quite similar to Purdue—a fledgling institution in a small farming town. The basic difference was that the Colorado community, on the Cache la Poudre River, obtained its water for agriculture from an irrigation system. Coming from the humid East, the Indianan knew little about the problems of the arid West, but he had practical experience both in farming and in river control. Although his academic duties had nothing to do with irrigation, Mead was fascinated by the developments in this field and assisted E. S. Nettleton, the newly appointed state engineer, in superintending the distribution of water in the Fort Collins area.[12]

Larimer County, where Fort Collins was located, provided Mead with his initial experience in dealing with the arid regions of the country. The first large-scale irrigation in the West, outside of the Mormons in Utah, began here, and here a dispute led to the first statewide system of public control of water rights. Colorado had enacted legislation for the orderly distribution of streams for irrigation as early as 1861, but not until the late 1870s did an increase in the size of ditches necessitate actual regulation. The problem began when the Union Colony founded Greeley in 1870 and dug a large diversion ditch from the Cache la Poudre River. Two years later, John C. Abbott and Benjamin H. Eaton went upstream and built the Lake Canal. Meanwhile, General R. A. Cameron organized the Larimer County Land Improvement Company, boomed Fort Collins, and in 1873–74 built a canal larger than the Lake Canal. This activity resulted in a heated controversy between Greeley and Fort Collins over water rights, with Greeley demanding recognition of the principle that priority of appropriation gave priority of use. The issue was temporarily solved because Fort Collins acquiesced to Greeley's demand for water. Then, in 1878, Eaton started to construct an even larger canal farther up the river. This proved to be the catalyst in formulating a system for public administration of water rights in Colorado.[13]

The Colorado constitution of 1876 had recognized the principle of priority of appropriation and asserted that the right to divert unappropriated water to the beneficial use of the people should never be denied. As the result of the Eaton scheme, however, legislation was enacted which clearly defined what became known as the Colorado System. In 1879, ten water districts—most of them covering an entire watershed—were established, with a state commissioner to divide the water according to the prior rights of the various ditches. The state district courts, acting as administrative boards, then issued decrees allocating priorities. After two exceptionally dry seasons, additional laws were passed which provided for lawsuits to challenge priorities, set up the office of state engineer to measure streams, created water divisions for the South Platte, Arkansas, and Rio Grande basins, and required that any person appropriating water file a record of it in the county clerk's office.[14]

Mead's only official contact with these regulations was as a part-time watershed engineer in Larimer County. At the same time, he was also assisting President Ingersoll and Professors A. E. Blount and James Cassidy in the organization of an agricultural experiment station for the community. These two activities complemented one another, as this locale essentially was devoted to irrigated farming. This stirred Mead's interest in the whole issue of water rights in arid areas, and came to occupy increasing amounts of his time away from his teaching duties. His primary responsibility, however, was in the classroom.[15]

Mead was popular with the students at Colorado State. His introduction as a faculty member came the morning after he arrived there. He and his bride lived in the dormitory, and they came down after everyone else had begun breakfast. With an "intriguing smile," the five-foot, seven-inch blond professor bowed formally, introduced Mrs. Mead, and then greeted each person in the room individually. Every morning thereafter, Mead spoke briefly to each student until, within a short time, he knew everyone's name. Debonair and approachable, he commanded respect and confidence from the entire campus community. He and Florence further endeared themselves to the students when they became the first faculty members to attend the occasional student dances.[16]

Because of limited funds and small enrollments, Colorado State, like almost all such colleges during that period, required their professors to teach a wide variety of subjects. Mead was hired to instruct in mathematics and physics, but one semester he gave the course in physiology, about which he admitted he knew practically nothing. Physics presented a special problem. As Mead later recollected, he performed "something of a stunt" by teaching it without any apparatus. Part of the course was devoted to "lessons in measurement and flow of water for irrigation." Mead lost few opportunities to discuss this all-important topic.[17]

After three semesters at Fort Collins, Mead resigned and moved back East. In 1883 he received a civil engineering degree from Iowa Agricultural College at Ames, and was awarded a master of science from Purdue the following year. But he still had not decided on a career. He liked teaching, but he had also liked engineering and farming. He had returned to Indiana mainly at the urging of Hiram Chase, his father-in-law, who wanted him to form a partnership in his legal firm. Mead "read" law under Chase, and even tried one case—which he lost. Apparently it was not discouragement over this failure, however, as much as it was ill health and interest in irrigation that caused him to look westward again. In July of 1885, the Meads moved back to Colorado.[18]

Mead's return to the East had not been a total loss. In addition to his graduate degrees from Purdue and Iowa State, he had acquired a valuable knowledge of law. This combination of legal and scientific skills would stand him in good stead in the years ahead. He began working for Colorado State Engineer Nettleton as his assistant, and then in the fall of 1885 he was reappointed to the faculty at Fort Collins. As his place in mathematics had been filled, President Ingersoll, who was eager to have Mead back, named him professor of irrigation engineering. It was the first such position in the United States.[19]

At the age of twenty-two, Mead finally had found his life's work. His two jobs, as a teacher and as assistant state engineer, enabled him to devote all of his energies to one end—"the study of all the physical, human and legal problems of turning on water with a shovel." The dual occupations complemented one another. In preparing his lectures, Mead became intrigued with the history of irrigation, and began studying the water laws of other countries. This not only made his classes more interesting, but it aided him in making recommendations for the improvement of Colorado water statutes. Nor were his courses confined to the building. Students (and even girls enrolled!) found themselves out in the field with Mead, gauging water flow, examining irrigated fields, and on one occasion fighting their way into cattails to conduct surveys for draining the swampy streams that ran through the campus.[20]

Mead spent his summers as an assistant state engineer, overseeing irrigation activities in the South Platte Valley. The task acquainted him with both the benefits and the shortcomings of Colorado's water laws. At this time, a major controversy was developing over the increasing power of the ditch operators. Their customers confronted these "water barons" in a so-called antiroyalty movement. Mead studied the problem, and as his ideas matured, he supported the position of the irrigators. He explained his views in a widely publicized address to a Farmers' Institute at Fort Collins in 1887.[21]

In his remarks, which were later disseminated as a pamphlet,

Mead warned against a dangerous trend he saw emerging. When irrigation first began, canal construction was a cooperative venture of users, and, in essence, the land and water went together. As the agricultural possibilities of the state became known, however, an era of speculative building took place, and canals gridironed the state. The companies that constructed these systems believed that by securing the water rights, they could control land values and earn tremendous profits. The cost of water rose with advances in real estate prices.[22]

Such speculative activity discouraged immigration, Mead said, and hindered the development of Colorado. Besides, it created an intolerable burden on the farmers who held contracts with these companies. Echoing the words of Major John Wesley Powell, the first national figure concerned with the arid West, Mead stressed that "the right to use water should inhere in the land to be irrigated, and water rights should go with land titles." In this address, and in his travels throughout the state, Mead urged farmers to lend their influence to secure legislation favorable to guarding and protecting the interests of the actual user against a "water-right aristocracy."[23]

Colorado enacted no additional water legislation while Mead was there, but in 1888 and 1889, the state Supreme Court declared that ditch companies were common carriers only, and the carrier could not become the proprietor of the water diverted. How much influence the young assistant state engineer had on these decisions cannot be ascertained, but their effect was to prevent the monopoly he warned against.[24]

Elwood Mead spent three years in his dual role as assistant state engineer and professor of irrigation engineering. In that time, his reputation as an authority on irrigation and water rights spread beyond the borders of Colorado. Wyoming leaders had consulted him when they created the office of territorial engineer, and upon setting up that position in 1888, they offered him the job. Colorado had been a valuable training ground, but this was an attractive opportunity. In Wyoming he could influence and direct irrigation along the lines that he felt were necessary if irrigation were to become an important and stable factor in western development. Elwood Mead moved to Cheyenne.

TWO

Wyoming Decade

WHEN MEAD ACCEPTED THE APPOINTMENT AS Wyoming's first territorial engineer in 1888, he hoped to play a more active role in influencing irrigation law and development than he had in Colorado. The water code in Wyoming was almost the same as the one in Colorado that he found so flawed, but he got the opportunity to correct these problems when Wyoming became a state in 1890. Mead wrote the constitutional provisions on water rights, and organized a system for the orderly division of streams. Through this work he earned a national reputation, and became a prominent spokesman for irrigation in the United States. For the next ten years, he was also involved in developing ideas to transform Wyoming into a prosperous agricultural state.

The year Mead arrived in Wyoming he found the territory in economic and political turmoil and change. The previous winter, one of the worst recorded in the American West, had seen chilling cold decimate large herds of cattle throughout the Northern Plains. Although Wyoming lost only 15 percent of its livestock, the value of the remaining animals fell by at least 30 percent. Ranching practices were undergoing a complete reappraisal, especially since experts claimed that the need for water was as important a factor as lack of food in the deaths of the steers. Moreover, the political power of Wyoming cattlemen was significantly diminished, but not broken, as the result of these economic setbacks.[1]

In 1888 a political struggle among Democrats, Republicans, and Governor Thomas Moonlight dominated the Wyoming political scene. A year earlier President Grover Cleveland had appointed Moonlight, a recently defeated Kansas politician, to be territorial governor after Wyoming Democrats failed to agree on a resident nominee. When the legislature convened in January, the Republicans controlled the upper house, the Democrats had a majority in the lower chamber, and Governor Moonlight seemingly pleased no one. In fact, his appointment and subsequent opposition to almost everything the legislators proposed proved to be a stimulus to the growing movement for statehood. In the meantime, the deadlock stymied meaningful legislation. The only positive result of this stormy session was a bill creating the office of territorial engineer, enacted largely through the efforts of James A. Johnston, Gibson Clark, and Francis E. Warren.[2]

Both Johnston and Clark had lived in Fort Collins, knew Professor Mead, and urged the governor to name him to the new post. Moonlight, regarded as a carpetbagger by many, was reluctant to appoint another outsider, but finally he relented to the persistent pressure from the two men. The territorial council confirmed the nomination by a seven-to-five vote in March of 1888, and Moonlight offered Mead the job for two years at an annual salary of twenty-five hundred dollars. Before accepting the position, Mead went to Cheyenne to meet the territorial officials. The governor was concerned about the engineer looking so young and told him in private that he hoped Mead would decline the proffered post because he was sure he would be a failure. Francis Warren, meanwhile, went to Fort Collins on business, and met Mead for the first time. He too was struck by his youthful appearance—Warren later said Mead was "still wearing pinafores" when he came to Wyoming—but he saw great possibilities for the thirty-year-old professor and urged him to accept.[3]

Mead was familiar with the water procedures in Wyoming when he moved to Cheyenne and took up his duties. The territorial water laws, adopted in 1886, were practically a copy of the Colorado code. Under these statutes, the territorial engineer's office oversaw the "supervision of the diversion and distribution of the public waters." It was a big job; Wyoming surpassed all the states and territories of the arid region in the number of streams available for irrigation. It had been divided into four water districts, and included over four hundred streams from which water was being diverted. Mead's first task was to determine the amount of water available, how much had been appropriated, and the extent of irrigable lands. During the summer of 1888 he traveled throughout the territory in a horse and buggy, inspecting ditches, gauging streams, and examining water titles. That fall, in his first annual report to the governor, Mead estimated that a million and a half acres were capable of being irrigated with the existing ditches, but that was only a small fraction of the potential. With proper development, he optimistically observed, Wyoming could "take rank as an important agricultural commonwealth."[4]

In the same report to Governor Moonlight, Mead called attention to specific deficiencies in Wyoming's water laws. He had experienced similar shortcomings in Colorado, but took this opportunity to review the problems with an eye to paving the way for reform. The trouble with all irrigation regulation in the United States, he said, was that it had been tentative and fragmentary. No attempt had been made to frame a complete water code; statutes had been enacted as needed. In the preceding decade, however, legislation had not kept pace with the rapid increase in irrigation. Wyoming had perhaps the best water laws in the arid West, but they too were inadequate.[5]

Mead's summer travels demonstrated the problems he faced in trying to bring order to the existing rules. For example, a person acquired a water right in Wyoming by posting a notice of intent at the point of diversion and then registering his claim with the appropriate county clerk. When Mead sought to compile a record of water filings, he discovered over three thousand claims with varying degrees of precision as to the amount appropriated, the ditch location, and the date of initial diversion. Irrigators had no idea how to measure the capacity of their ditch, the amount of water needed, or the amount used. The units registered in the clerk's offices included square inches, agricultural inches, California inches, and miner's inches—in a territory where the law recognized only cubic feet per second. Claims escalated all the way from a reasonable amount up to the entire flow of a stream. If the amount of water claimed actually existed, Mead observed, Wyoming would have been a lake.[6]

Mead's attempt to plat the diversion ditches presented another difficulty. County surveyors were supposed to certify the capacity of the ditches, but this was often done without actual inspection. Mead found a record giving the location of one division "at the place where I now stand." Another said the ditch was somewhere on the western slope of the Big Horn Mountains. Equally frustrating was the determination of priorities. Many streams flowed through several counties, so that the records might be found in as many as six places. In addition, there was confusion about the method of dating diversions. Did one's claim begin when he announced his intention to build a ditch, when he finished it, or when he first applied water to the land?[7]

Adjudication of conflicting claims fell to district judges, who had no competence in irrigation matters. They handed down decrees, moreover, only to actual claimants before the court. One case that Mead discovered, for example, dealt with six of forty-two ditches on a stream, leaving the rest for future litigation. Nor were these judicial rulings consistent. An irrigator of three hundred acres was given five acre feet per second per day, while another with twenty-eight acres received eleven. When Mead assumed his duties, a mere 5 percent of water right priorities had been determined by the courts, and the attorney general advised him that, according to the law, the territorial engineer could not regulate the remaining 95 percent until the courts had ruled on them.[8]

The chaotic nature of the Wyoming water laws was frustrating, and Mead immediately set about to bring order to the system. He compiled lists of diversions on each stream and arranged them according to priority. He set up instruments and began measuring the flow on all the waterways in the territory to determine just how much water was available. He also devised a standard form for claims, so that water applications would contain all the data necessary to determine rights. These actions were a beginning, but, as Mead told Moonlight in his 1888 report, what was really needed was a comprehensive water code. Fortunately, the opportunity to formulate such a law came the next year.[9]

In April of 1889, Francis E. Warren succeeded Moonlight as governor and soon thereafter issued a call for a convention to meet in September at Cheyenne to draft a state constitution. These actions were the result of the election of 1888, which brought Republican Benjamin Harrison to the White House and G.O.P. control of both houses of Congress. This paved the way for the admission of six predominantly Republican territories into the Union during the first two years of Harrison's tenure as president. Wyoming was one of these. The state constitution that the delegates produced in the fall of 1889 was unremarkable except for the part that dealt with water laws. Here, the ideas of Elwood Mead were adopted almost exactly as he proposed them.[10]

Mead was not a member of the convention, but the committee on agriculture, irrigation, and water rights was chaired by James A. Johnston, one of those responsible for his appointment as territorial engineer. Another supporter was Charles H. Burritt, a lawyer from Johnson County, who became the spokesman for this committee in convention debate. These men met nightly with Mead and hammered out an effective statement that would end confusion in the water code. Their major political concern was opposition from the legal profession, which conducted a lucrative

business in defending irrigation claims. However, when the prestigious law firm of Lacey and VanDevanter endorsed their ideas,
this apprehension vanished and swung the balance. The proposition (Article 8) that dealt with irrigation and water rights was
adopted by the delegates by a thirty-five to two vote.[11]

Article 8 declared the water of all natural streams, springs, and
lakes to be the property of the state. It established the principle of
priority of appropriation for beneficial use as the basis of claims
for this resource, and set up a board of control to supervise the
appropriation, distribution, and diversion of water. This panel
consisted of the superintendents of the four existing water districts
in the state and the state engineer, who was to serve as its president. The decisions of the board were subject to review by the
state courts. Wyoming voters approved the constitution in November of 1889.[12]

On July 10, 1890, President Harrison signed the statehood bill,
putting the constitution into effect. Mead was named state engineer by Governor Warren, and his suggestions for implementing
Article 8 were enacted into law by the first Wyoming state legislature. According to these statutes, a person desiring water was to
file an application with the state engineer's office, showing the location and nature of the proposed distributing works, the amount
needed, and the purpose for which it was to be used. If the claim
was not detrimental to the public interest and water was available,
the applicant could begin construction of his diversion ditch. The
state engineer's office awarded a final certification when the water
began to be used in accordance with the original request.[13]

Mead next turned his attention to the problem of clearing up
water-rights claims made prior to statehood. Many were extravagant grants that bore little or no relation to actual conditions. On
January 1, 1891, the board of control took charge of the adjudication of these. Mead and the four water-district superintendents
proceeded to measure the ditches and survey the irrigated and irrigable lands of appropriators. Next they compiled charts showing

the amounts of water available, the amounts claimed, and the amounts actually needed. They sent irrigators blank forms to record the details of their claims. At meetings around the state, Mead and his assistants explained to farmers that they would receive only a small percentage of their rights if all recorded grants were honored. For example, of the 132 irrigators on one stream, there was actually enough water for the first 6 or 7, if they were given the amount claimed in their original applications. The other 125 would have to buy water from them.[14]

Mead pointed out that with an equitable distribution of water there was plenty for all if excessive claims were disallowed. He based his calculations for beneficial use on the "duty of water" (the amount needed to irrigate an acre) at one acre foot for seventy acres. Moreover, the cost of securing rights under this system was the nominal fees for filing, in marked contrast to the expensive litigation characteristic of cases under the old system. The earliest appropriators immediately complained, but a majority either recognized that their claims were not justified, felt the pressure of neighbors who would be squeezed out if they prevailed, or recognized that the legal costs would be prohibitive should they try to press the issue. In fact, the whole process tended to disarm most critics by its order and efficiency. A few cases were appealed, but by the end of 1894 over 60 percent of the unadjudicated claims had been settled by the state board, compared with only 5 percent in the preceding five years when the courts made the determinations.[15]

The adoption of Article 8, enactment of measures to implement it, and the settlement of claims made prior to 1890 placed Wyoming at the forefront of irrigation development in the nation. At age thirty-six, Elwood Mead had made a significant contribution not only to the water laws of Wyoming but ultimately to all of the western United States, and indeed to arid regions around the world. The Wyoming Code and the administrative system he devised came to be known as the Wyoming System. It was the model for similar legislation in the rest of the arid American West. Its influence soon spilled across the border into Canada where it formed the basis of the water laws for that country's emerging irrigation development. Ultimately, Mead's ideas spread as far as the southern hemisphere, into Australia, New Zealand and South Africa.[16]

Mead's accomplishments in the field of irrigation were only part of his contributions to Wyoming. Its admission to the Union in 1890 coincided with several national developments that would have a significant impact on the young state. By the last decade of the nineteenth century, the frontier in American history was gone. This was true not only of traditional farmland, but of easily and inexpensively irrigated acreage as well. In Wyoming, most of this type of irrigable land was claimed by speculators who used their holdings to keep settlers in a "water peonage" or by cattlemen who used it wastefully. Falling farm prices added to the problems that retarded the state's development at this time, a decline that culminated in the Panic of 1893. These factors conspired to keep Wyoming sparsely populated and economically stunted.[17]

As Mead surveyed the economic scene in Wyoming, he saw a way to fulfill one of the goals he had envisioned in his first annual report in 1888; he wanted to make the state an agricultural commonwealth. He had seen in Colorado, and in some parts of Wyoming, the contented cultivator of his youth. He knew the blessings and benefits of irrigated agriculture. Now he wanted to adapt this farming method to the peculiar conditions of the region. As part of his idea, shortly after arriving in Wyoming, he induced farmers in different parts of the territory to experiment and keep records of the amount of water needed for various crops, and to test varieties of crops to evaluate what grew best in their areas.[18]

Ultimately, he hoped to see much of Wyoming divided into small irrigated farms on which these selected crops would be grown with larger contiguous areas of grazing lands. This plan was basically an application of ideas found in John Wesley Powell's

1878 *Report on the Lands of the Arid Regions of the United States.*
Powell believed that one way to develop the vast expanses west of
the 100th meridian was to combine farming and ranching in this
way. Mead saw the arrangement as the cornerstone of Wyoming's
future prosperity. It would provide the state with a home food
source, prevent another disaster to the range industry because of a
guaranteed feed supply, and attract people there.[19]

Wyoming had ample water for such a scheme. The problem was
that most of the undeveloped irrigable land left in the state was in
the hands of the federal government. To make these vast areas
productive, expensive works had to be built, but capital could not
be attracted to such ventures without guarantees that it could re-
cover its investment. Under existing federal statutes—the Homestead, Timber Culture, and Desert Land acts—a speculator could
acquire over one thousand acres of federal land under a ditch without any obligation to the irrigation company, even though the
company's development might increase land values as much as ten
or fifteen dollars an acre. The solution lay in an arrangement to
bring federal land and state water titles together.[20]

Mead was one of the earliest proponents of cession of federal
lands to the states. The failure of the Desert Land and Timber
Culture acts to further irrigation in the West had convinced him
of the ineffectiveness of national policies. The states, he believed,
were best able to deal with the land problems peculiar to their
locale. Besides, he argued, if the federal government should not or
would not develop these areas, it ought to give them to those who
would. Otherwise, the western states would remain forever under-
populated and underdeveloped. To Mead, the problem was more
than just making arid areas productive; there was a need to popu-
late these regions as well.[21]

Mead convinced his friend Governor Warren of the need for
federal land cessions, and worked closely with him on this matter.
In 1891, after he became a senator, Warren introduced a bill in
Congress calling for cession of federal lands to the states, with the

funds from the sale of such lands to be used to build irrigation facilities. Settlers would be limited to 160 acres of irrigated land. Later that year, Mead vigorously promoted the cession idea in Salt Lake City at the first National Irrigation Congress. This organization, founded largely at the instigation of William E. Smythe, a journalist with the *Omaha Bee,* adopted a resolution in favor of the cession plan. In spite of these efforts, however, Warren's bill did not pass—nor did his proposal the following year, one that called for the donation without restrictions of all arid lands to the states.[22]

In 1893, Elwood Mead attended another Irrigation Congress at Los Angeles, but by this time the proponents of a national approach had become hopelessly divided as to an appropriate policy. Mead was convinced that cession was necessary for the development of western states, and particularly for Wyoming. Opponents claimed that the action would mean that these lands would fall into the hands of jobbers and corporations. Others urged that the federal government build the necessary works. Fearing that a show of disunity would weaken chances for congressional action to aid the arid West, the delegates endorsed no specific proposition and instead appointed a commission to investigate conditions in each of the seventeen states and territories and to formulate a national plan. Meanwhile, Joseph M. Carey, Wyoming's other senator, attached to an appropriation bill an amendment bestowing one million acres on each state if the land were irrigated within three years and settled by farmers on small tracts.[23]

That both senators from Wyoming should introduce bills regarding irrigation showed its importance for the state, but it undoubtedly put Mead in a somewhat awkward position. By 1890 political differences between Carey and Warren had grown to open hostility. Mead remained friends with both men, indicative of the generally apolitical stance he was to maintain throughout his long public career. He was not enthusiastic about Carey's proposal, which he did not regard as "an adequate and altogether satisfactory solution of the land question." At his suggestion, the time allotted to complete the irrigation works was increased from three to ten years, and with that change Congress enacted the bill on August 18, 1894.[24]

Two weeks after the passage of the Carey Act, the third National Irrigation Congress met in Denver. There was still a wide divergence of opinion among the members as to the direction they should pursue on policy. Before the meeting opened, Mead wrote to friends that he was anxious to prevent "any unwise and unjudicious action" that would damage the cause of reclamation. His interest, he said, was only to see irrigation made a "safe and reasonably lucrative business." Above all, the Wyoming state engineer opposed federal involvement in constructing irrigation works. His experience with the engineers' corps had taught him "the enormous cost, extravagance and waste which characterizes national public works and the harrowing delay and uncertainty of work dependent on congressional appropriations." More importantly, he feared that such legislation would foster favoritism for the larger states—such as California—and result in a federal policy that could not be adapted to the needs of the diverse areas of the arid West.[25]

The Denver gathering was a success for those who wanted to give the Carey Act a "fair trial." After the meeting, Mead wrote his assistant, Frank Bond, that they "managed to prevent the people who still wanted unrestricted cession and the others who wanted the government to do everything to keep silent." Mead was especially critical of Smythe, whom he felt had "nothing in view except his own interests and the interests of [his propaganda magazine] *Irrigation Age*." He called Smythe "a visionary enthusiast who, if left alone, would make the whole movement ridiculous." In fact, by 1897, when the Irrigation Congress met in Cheyenne, Mead was thoroughly disenchanted with the "cheap crowd" that ran the organization. He felt that they were "simply concerned in the pickings which come from these Congresses and in exploiting themselves before the public."[26]

Meanwhile, Wyoming had proceeded with plans to take advantage of the Carey Act. Mead was responsible largely for formulating a state program and working with the Department of the Interior to guarantee that the provisions were met. Characteristically, the engineer predicted a surge of construction and immigration that would lead to "a new era of growth and prosperity for Wyoming." In 1896, his office had approved six private projects and the first entries were made. The most ambitious of these was in the Big Horn Basin, where William (Buffalo Bill) Cody launched a company that envisioned irrigating over 500,000 acres. Unfortunately, little private capital could be induced into such ventures. Applications for land were substantial, but less than 1 percent of the estimated twelve to fifteen million irrigable acres in Wyoming received final patent while Mead was state engineer.[27]

Mead had supported the Carey Act and was instrumental in its implementation in Wyoming, but he did not view it as the answer to the state's economic problems. The act provided assistance for reclamation, but did not address the unique needs of Wyoming. As early as 1893, Mead had noted that the open range was destructive to grazing lands, the great natural resource of the state. As long as the range was free, there would be no incentive to improve it or to reform wasteful practices. Everyone was out for himself. In 1897, Mead proposed that the millions of acres of public grazing land in Wyoming be given to the state to lease and the proceeds used to finance irrigation projects. Settlers could buy 160 irrigable acres and rent 2,560 acres of adjacent land for a cent an acre annually. The remaining public lands would be leased to prevent their destruction by the careless overgrazing of cattlemen and sheep ranchers. The idea of raising cattle on irrigated land and controlling the size of the herds grazed had grown out of the lessons of the disastrous winter of 1886–87. Mead also saw it as a way to end the long-standing conflict between sheepmen and cattle ranchers by assigning to each a specific area. Mead's ideas were given favorable notice in newspapers around the state, but nothing came of his proposals.[28]

By 1897, Elwood Mead had advanced professionally as far as he could in Wyoming. He had written the water code, set up the administration for running it, and formulated the state's participation under the Carey Act. That year his wife Florence died of a toxic goiter, leaving him with three small children under the age of seven. About the same time, he was reluctantly being drawn to the view that federal action was necessary to realize the full benefits of reclamation, and he naturally wanted to be involved. Mead began looking for new opportunities and challenges. In November, Senator Warren approached Secretary of Agriculture James A. Wilson about reestablishing the Division of Irrigation in his department. Wilson hired Mead as a part-time consultant until congressional approval of the plan was obtained early in 1899. Mead then resigned as state engineer and moved to Washington, D.C., to direct irrigation investigations.[29]

THREE

On the National Scene

BETWEEN 1899 AND 1907, ELWOOD MEAD SERVED
as full-time expert-in-charge of irrigation investigations for the
Office of Experiment Stations in the Department of Agriculture.
The appointment put him on the national scene at a time when
the federal government was moving toward direct involvement in
reclamation. Mead's opposition to large-scale federal action conflicted with influential advisors to President Theodore Roosevelt.
He became the spokesman for a limited, states-oriented program,
but his views did not prevail. After the passage of the Reclamation
Act of 1902, Mead began to look for other professional opportunities. Nevertheless, he stayed with the Agriculture Department
for five additional years. Meanwhile, he returned to the classroom,
teaching part-time at the University of California, Berkeley.[1]

By the late 1890s, as it became obvious that federal involvement
in reclamation loomed, attention centered around what form that
action would take and who would direct it. The Agriculture and
Interior departments had vied for over a decade to dominate
irrigation policy. Officials in each had distinct ideas as to its
scope, and now they sought to control whatever federal program
emerged. The creation of irrigation investigations, with Mead as
its head, was part of these bureaucratic manueverings. Ultimately,
proponents of a limited federal role hoped that the irrigations di-

vision would supervise the government's reclamation activities and that Mead would run it.[2]

In his position as head of irrigation investigations, Mead's primary focus was on the application of water to the land. He realized early in his career that irrigation farmers required specialized help and advice. He had begun to explore this need in Wyoming, where he induced a number of farmers to experiment with different crops and methods of irrigation. The mandates of his new federal job were to gather and disseminate information primarily of interest to the small irrigator. His duties included ascertaining the most economical use of water for the cultivation of different crops in various regions, analyzing soils, and determining the fruits, grains, and vegetables that grow best under irrigation. Mead was also to examine the laws concerning water rights in the arid regions, to point out defects in them or their administration, and to assist farmers in securing and protecting their rights. Agricultural colleges and experiment stations throughout the nation were to cooperate in carrying out these tasks.[3]

At the same time, as a complement to Mead's assignment, Frederick Haynes Newell, head of the Geological Survey (in the Interior Department), was to examine the fluvial system of the West. This included studying the quantity and value of rainfall and the water from melting snows, the courses and habits of streams, the area that could be irrigated by them, and the best methods of distribution. In addition, Newell was to prepare a hydrographic map to assist in utilizing these waters for agriculture. Mead's group, then, concerned itself with the practical aspects of irrigation, while Newell's staff dealt with the technical.[4]

Several important flaws marred the cooperation implied by this arrangement. For one thing, bureaucratic rivalry and jealousy caused friction as the two groups competed for funds and responsibility. Moreover, Mead and Newell had serious personal and ideological differences. Privately, Mead had been critical of the work of the Geological Survey for a long time. In 1895, for example,

Newell had asked Mead for help in securing appropriations to continue stream gauging by the Geological Survey. In seeking assistance on this matter from Wyoming's Senator Carey, Mead gave half-hearted support, noting that although he had a poor opinion of the topological surveys made under Newell's supervision, he felt Newell's stream-gauging work had "considerable practical value."[5]

In that same year, Mead began a movement to have the Geological Survey leave monuments or tracings in the field so that its work could be identified on the ground. Otherwise, he felt that the surveys had "no practical value." He even designed a marker to be placed at the corner of a township. Newell objected to the idea of placing markers, but when Congressman Frank Mondell of Wyoming introduced a bill to require them Newell wrote that he was adopting the idea. In March of 1896, Mead wrote a friend, O. V. P. Stout, that he was gratified "after twenty years of blindness on this matter that the light should at last penetrate the recesses of the survey." Still, he persisted, calling it "only prudent" that Congress should place the matter beyond question by the enactment of a law.[6]

Mead's interference probably irritated Newell, but not so much as the creation of Irrigation Investigations. This division took a sizable part of his duties, and he complained to both Mead and Secretary of Agriculture James Wilson. He told Wilson that Mead was trying to draft engineers from the Geological Survey. Mead denied this and pleaded with Newell to end the "bickering" between them. This was to no avail.[7]

Ideologically, the split between the two men was more serious, because the conception of reclamation that Mead held was far different than that of Newell and his associates. The Geological Survey looked at irrigation from an engineering standpoint, and seemed to be interested in building dams and reservoirs to cover the largest area possible with water. Mead, on the other hand, was more conservative in his approach. He agreed that federal construction of reservoirs was needed to regulate the flow of streams and obtain maximum use of the water, but he emphasized that these facilities should be directed at solving existing problems and improving already functioning projects, not at launching new programs.[8]

Mead's ideas eventually put him in disfavor with George Maxwell, another leader of the reclamation movement and founder of the National Irrigation Association in 1897. The drive for federal involvement in reclamation had begun that year with Captain Hiram W. Chittenden's report on his survey of possible reservoir sites in Wyoming and Colorado. Mead had accompanied Chittenden on his inspection tour of Wyoming, and the two men agreed on basic fundamentals. Chittenden urged the government to construct storage reservoirs to regulate the flow of streams and for flood control, but to leave irrigation matters to the states. Capitalizing on the publicity from Chittenden's recommendations, Maxwell, a lawyer turned lobbyist, set out to convince eastern legislators and businessmen of the benefits that would accrue to the rest of the country from reclamation in the West. His organization, a supplement to the dying National Irrigation Congress, sought federal aid for reclamation. The mainstay of his support came from the five transcontinental railroads that crossed the arid region. Each contributed five hundred dollars a month to finance his activities.[9]

When he first learned of the proposed financial arrangement between Maxwell and the railroads in 1899, Mead wrote to H. G. Burt, president of the Union Pacific, and outlined his own views—and his objections to Maxwell's concept of the problems of the arid region. Mead favored letting the western states lease the lands within their boundaries for grazing, with the federal government retaining title. The proceeds would be used by the states to build reservoirs and other appurtenances, while the federal government would construct a limited number of works that could be classed as necessary for flood control or navigation. These projects would be justified in the same manner as river and harbor improvements in the eastern states.[10]

According to Mead, Maxwell's program was based on an entirely different concept. Maxwell made government reservoirs the principal feature, but Mead feared that federal control of irrigation would be the ultimate result of such undertakings. Maxwell stated that sales from reclaimed land would return a larger sum than expended, and he estimated that 100 million dollars could be added to the treasury by this program. Mead exposed the fallacy in this, pointing out that if private enterprise had not earned profits from irrigation projects, it was foolish to expect the government to do so. Reservoirs were demanded not by people who desired to occupy land but by those who already owned land with an insufficient water supply. Moreover, Maxwell wanted a survey of all the land to be reclaimed, with plans for all of the necessary work to be drawn by the federal government. Mead argued that the irrigable areas were known, and if the states were going to build the reservoirs they ought to prepare the plans themselves.[11]

In the beginning, relations between Maxwell and Mead remained friendly, at least on the surface. Maxwell had written a warm letter of endorsement in 1898 to Secretary of Agriculture Wilson when Mead was mentioned for the irrigation investigations position. Two years later, however, the amity ended as the two increasingly clashed over their views of reclamation. The split became open in 1900, when the National Irrigation Congress planned to meet in Chicago. Mead, who was president of the organization, asked J. S. Dennis, an irrigation expert from Canada, to speak on his country's irrigation laws, which had been patterned after Wyoming's statutes. Maxwell, who was executive chairman, accidently intercepted Dennis's acceptance. He accused Mead and Dennis of having an understanding regarding the discussion of international water rights at the conference, an issue Maxwell hoped to avoid so as not to complicate efforts for national reclamation. Mead denied any collusion, but he was forced to withdraw his invitation. Relations between Maxwell and him degenerated thereafter. In the meantime, at the Chicago meeting, the Irrigation Congress dropped its demands for cession to the states and urged federal reclamation of the arid West.[12]

Both major political parties in 1900 endorsed some type of federal action in reclamation. Two of the most prominent proponents of such policy, Newell and Maxwell, were close friends of Chief Forester Gifford Pinchot, himself an intimate of Theodore Roosevelt. Irrigationists had always stressed the importance of preserving the forested watersheds as part of their program. Leaders in the western states, however, had opposed attempts to close the public domain, claiming that the act would retard their economic development. These conflicting ideas complicated united western action on this matter. Meanwhile, in 1901, Representative Francis G. Newlands of Nevada introduced a bill providing that the money from land sales be spent on reclamation projects. This legislation was defeated in the Senate in March. In September, however, when Roosevelt—with his strong conservation bent—became president, he seized the opportunity to combine the two issues—closing the forest lands and opening the arid acres. In so doing, he focused attention on the entire question of the public domain.[13]

Roosevelt, in his autobiography published in 1916, credited Newell and Pinchot with formulating his conservation and irrigation policy, and for furnishing the material on it for his first state of the union message in 1901. This was only partly true. Others were consulted and offered ideas. For example, Francis Warren and Frank Mondell, both prominent and powerful legislators, insisted on more local autonomy than the Newlands bill provided. They had been long-time friends of Mead who had obviously shaped their approach to reclamation. Senator Warren talked to the president and suggested that Mead's views be solicited. Roosevelt was already acquainted with Mead through Benjamin Ide Wheeler, president of the University of California at Berkeley. After a lengthy interview, the chief executive asked Mead to submit ideas for inclusion in his message to Congress. The irrigation expert wrote a letter outlining his views, and his assistant, Frank Adams, handcarried it to the White House. Mead then conferred with Secretary of Agriculture Wilson about his conversation with

Roosevelt so their recommendations might be harmonious. Later, he learned from Warren that the president had reflected on Mead's ideas and recast his message to incorporate most of them.[14]

The irrigation section of Roosevelt's message contained the unmistakable imprint of Mead's ideas. In fact, parts appear to be almost direct quotes from things Mead had been enunciating as far back as 1887. These ideas were, moreover, the very aspects of the Newlands Act that concerned Warren and many other westerners. The most important of these was the call to respect existing state water laws and the need to reform them where necessary (including an oblique reference to the Wyoming system as a role model). In addition, the president cautioned restraint in attempting too much federal action too fast. Finally, in recognizing the cost as well as equating justification for these projects to river and harbor activities in the East, he called for repayment "so far as possible by the land reclaimed." This latter proposition was a clear rejoinder to Newell and Maxwell, who had talked of sums up to 100 million dollars being earned from reclaimed lands.[15]

As legislation to implement federal involvement moved through Congress, Mead advised and consulted on it with many lawmakers, especially westerners. While he publicly supported the general principle, the irrigation expert's approach was much more conservative than Newlands, Maxwell, or Newell. Francis E. Warren was leading forces pushing the so-called State Engineers' Bill, a law along the lines advocated by Mead. It passed the Senate in March of 1902. Unfortunately, shortly thereafter, Mrs. Warren became ill and died, causing the senator to be absent from Washington for over a month. According to two historians who have studied the passage of this legislation, Newlands and Roosevelt used this opportunity to flatter and use Mondell to get what they wanted. They claim Roosevelt "so dazzled Mondell with praise and publicity that the congressman (whom the president had requested personally to manage the floor fight) agreed to follow Roosevelt's desire to change what he described as some of 'the phraseology' in Warren's bill." It essentially amounted to a substitution of the Newlands bill for Warren's proposal.[16]

Privately, Mead had a poor opinion of Mondell and feared that his association with him might have adverse repercussions. The Wyoming congressman already had quarreled with Roosevelt over a bill to transfer the Forest Service to the Agriculture Department because of his dislike of Pinchot. In a letter to University of California President Wheeler, Mead indicated his fear that Pinchot would think he had influence on Mondell. Characterizing the Wyoming congressman as "opinionated and somewhat bumptious," Mead said that if he had exerted influence Mondell would have kept out of both forestry and irrigation "because he don't [*sic*] know enough about either to deal with them intelligently." Nevertheless, Roosevelt was now using him to get reclamation legislation enacted.[17]

As the Newlands bill neared final passage, Mead distanced himself from it more and more. He confided to Wheeler that owing to the "recent disclosures of the strength of the Railroad Lobby and its ability to control the location of irrigation works," he did not believe the legislation would pass. The country would "not lose much if it fails," he added. In February he had expressed similar sentiments to Wheeler, noting that the "foolish talk" about hundreds of millions of acres of land and hundreds of millions of dollars had scared eastern farmers sleepless. He did not care if the bill was defeated because "there was too much demogogy [*sic*] and dishonesty in this campaign . . . for one to enthuse over it." Mead's 1902 report on the activities of his department described a number of successful private irrigation projects, and contained a veiled hint that the federal government would do well to keep out of irrigation.[18]

On June 17, 1902, the Newlands Act passed Congress, and the president signed it shortly thereafter. This law established a revolving fund of revenue from the sale of public land. These monies were to be used to build major reclamation works in the West, with the water users expected to repay construction costs over a

ten-year period. These receipts then would be added to the fund
to finance additional facilities. The legislation also provided for
homestead entry onto these lands without commutation and limited the amount of land any one landowner could irrigate to 160
acres. Farmers were expected to build their own distribution canals and prepare the land for cultivation. Finally, the secretary of
the interior was given the discretion to begin works as soon as he
deemed them economically feasible and to establish the necessary
agency to direct such activities.[19]

The bill had several serious flaws that plagued reclamation for
over a quarter of a century. In order to placate all of the western
states, the law called for the expenditure of the funds within each
state in proportion to the sales of land in those states "as far as
practicable." This was unwise. Nevada, for example, had few lands
that anyone would purchase, and a great need for irrigation; Oklahoma had considerable land sales and little need for irrigation.
Added to this was the pressure from every state to benefit as soon
as possible, and the discretion allowed the secretary of the interior
to begin works that he felt were financially feasible. The result was
twenty-four projects begun within five years, far above need and
even farther above estimated costs.[20]

As the federal government launched this frenzy of construction,
Mead was effectively shunted aside, even though his status was
upgraded in 1902 to chief of irrigation investigations. After Newell
was appointed head of the Reclamation Service, he tried to have
Mead's job abolished. He was unsuccessful, and Mead continued
to do what he could to improve the conditions for the small
settler, and to address the larger issues created by the expanded
role of the federal government in western waters.[21]

The federal government's involvement in large-scale irrigation
projects widened the scope of allocation conflicts. Problems Mead
had solved on the intrastate streams of Wyoming became magni-
fied as interstate watershed development proceeded. Squabbles
arose between states over the distribution of the increased water

that huge reservoirs made possible. Mead's expertise was sought as these disputes reached the courts. He testified in a number of cases, the most notable being *Kansas v. Colorado* which temporarily settled a conflict between these two states, but which showed the potential for endless litigation. Recognizing the need to prevent this, Mead headed a committee appointed by the National Irrigation Congress in 1906 to propose a remedy. He and his committee recommended a federal administrative system similar to the Wyoming System, an idea that ultimately resulted in numerous interstate watershed compacts. Mainly, however, Mead concentrated on his official duties.[22]

The scope of irrigation investigations had steadily expanded since 1898, when Congress appropriated ten thousand dollars to look into water-rights problems in the arid states. That sum was raised to thirty-five thousand dollars in 1900, and to fifty thousand dollars the following year. In 1899, Mead had made a study of water rights in the Big Horn Mountains and on the Missouri River, as well as a general investigation of the use of water for irrigation. These reports were so well received that a group of prominent Californians petitioned Dr. A. C. True, director of Experiment Stations, to have Mead do a thorough survey of irrigation in that state with the goal of reforming water laws there. After the governor vetoed a bill to fund this study, the California Water and Forest Association raised ten thousand dollars to help finance the survey, and professors from Stanford and the University of California, Berkeley, agreed to work on the project.[23]

One of the main backers of the state survey was President Wheeler of Berkeley. He was concerned that everyone in the state recognized the importance of irrigation, but his institution was contributing very little to its development. Wheeler decided to establish a Department of Irrigation and offered Mead a professorship in November 1900. Mead declined noting that while he was tempted he had several projects that prevented him from accepting. He wanted to finish a general study of the problems of the arid region. In addition, he wished to complete the California investigation then under way, as well as one started in Utah, and see them reach "printer's ink." Furthermore, the Department of Agriculture had arranged for him to go to Europe in 1901 to study water laws and customs there, and he did not want to lose that opportunity.[24]

Mead, however, did agree to come to Berkeley in the spring of 1901 and present a six-week course, and to supervise the organization of the department that the president desired. Wheeler appointed him Professor of the Institutions and Practice of Irrigation. Mead's lectures proved to be popular, and in 1903 they were published as *Irrigation Institutions*. The book received widespread acclaim and was regarded as an authority on the laws and principles governing the use and proprietorship of water for reclamation. He planned to return to the university again in the spring of 1902.[25]

Shortly after returning to Washington from California, Mead attended a baseball game, one of his favorite hobbies. He caught a trolley car for home, and as it neared an intersection where he was to transfer, he saw the other car and feared that he would miss it. A man who deplored wasting time, he jumped from his car and dashed to the other. As he started to climb aboard, Mead lost his balance and fell beneath the trolley. One wheel passed over his outstretched right arm, nearly severing it. He was rushed to a hospital where the crushed limb was amputated. Mead accepted the misfortune with characteristic good nature, writing Wheeler that "if I understand my field, I can do as well without any hands as with both of them." Perhaps he thought of that other one-armed giant of the arid region, John Wesley Powell. Summoning Frank Adams from California, Mead went to Atlantic City to recuperate and to learn to write with his left hand.[26]

While recovering from this tragedy, Mead had time to reflect on his future. He continued to be torn between his work with the Agriculture Department and a desire to return to the classroom.

He had given special courses at Harvard in 1901 and 1902, and officials there urged him to join their staff, but he declined because he preferred his arrangements with California. Mead oversaw the operations of the Irrigation Department at Berkeley closely. Although he was on campus intermittently, he took an active interest in the curriculum and in procuring people to teach courses. The personnel of the Irrigation Investigations staff in California assisted him and filled in whenever their boss could not meet his classes. Wheeler, anxious to have him as a regular member of the faculty, gave him wide leeway in arranging his commitments to the two jobs.[27]

Meanwhile, the one-armed professor carried forward his work for the Agriculture Department with great vigor. He and those under him continued to survey water rights and methods of irrigation throughout the West. Mead was willing to look into anything that might aid the farmer. In 1900, for example, one of his bulletins discussed growing tea by irrigation, and two years later another examined rice cultivation. C. T. Johnson, an assistant, went to Egypt about this time, and Mead's travels to Italy resulted in voluminous reports on practices in those countries. Other bulletins dealt with practical matters such as building ditches and leveling land. Most people praised Mead's efforts, but Newell continued to watch him "like a hawk," and Maxwell tried to frustrate his plans whenever he could. After the passage of the Newlands Act, for example, Mead requested that more money be expended to prepare and advise the increased number of settlers about irrigation farming. Instead, it became more and more difficult to obtain congressional appropriations.[28]

As time went on, the attacks by Maxwell and Newell degenerated into personal haggling. In 1903 in California, Mead actively supported the Works Bill, an attempt to bring order to the state's water code along the lines of Wyoming's system. The proposed legislation was the outgrowth of the study financed by the Water and Forest Association, and was drawn up by a group of men including Mead, Wheeler, and Newell. Nevertheless, Maxwell used Mead's involvement as an excuse to discredit him. He supplied ammunition that attacked the proposed legislation—and specifically the irrigation investigations chief—to most newspapers in California. Many journals, especially in the southern half of the state, used the material. The editor of the *Los Angeles Times,* for example, demanded to know why Mead, an official of the Agriculture Department, was interfering in California's affairs. Maxwell sent clippings of this and similar editorials to Secretary Wilson. The controversy became quite heated, but Mead stood his ground and his superiors in Washington backed him. When his connection with the university was assailed, he offered to resign, but Wheeler would not hear of it.[29]

The unpleasant aspects of fighting for what he believed in were frustrating, but there were compensations. In 1904, Purdue University recognized Mead's accomplishments in irrigation by conferring on him its first honorary doctorate in engineering. Mead was extremely proud of this honor from his alma mater, and was thereafter called "Doctor." The title enhanced his name, but did not improve his position.[30]

The bickering and the annual fight for appropriations bothered Mead, and he found the administrative chores time-consuming and oppressive. He had less and less time for research and writing. He wanted to go to Berkeley full time, but officials there could not match his government salary of three thousand dollars. After the San Francisco earthquake in 1906, the university budget became even tighter, and Wheeler asked Mead to forgo his one thousand dollar stipend that year, saying that he did not devote enough time to his duties. The investigations chief did some consulting work for New York and Boston financiers, and flirted briefly with the idea of going into private industry—one of the few times he considered leaving public service.[31]

Mead was a shrewd businessman who managed his personal finances remarkably well. Many of his investments were in real estate and he generally realized a good return on his money. In 1891, he purchased two farms adjoining his father's land in Indiana, and in both cases he bought them for a price below their value. While in Wyoming, he invested in irrigation projects; at one time, he owned 1,000 acres on Elkhorn Creek. Later he became a partner in a canal company and purchased a 169-acre farm. After he joined the Agriculture Department in 1899, he subscribed five thousand dollars for land company stock in California. Mead made no secret of these holdings or of his consultations for private firms, although such activities would appear to raise questions of conflict of interest and cast doubts on his inveigling against land speculators. He justified his profits because he firmly believed that persons who risked capital in irrigation were entitled to adequate returns as long as they were not at the expense of settlers. Moreover, Mead always had an abundance of enemies ready to discredit him if he took advantage of his position or made excessive profits.[32]

By 1906, Mead was becoming restless and cast about for a new endeavor. On September 28 of that year, he married Mary Lewis of Scranton, Pennsylvania, who had been a surgical nurse at the operation in which his arm was amputated. He began a "second family," and this, of course, raised his living expenses. The University of California was not in a position to pay him what he considered to be adequate, and his future in Washington was not promising. Then, in October, state officials in Victoria, Australia, invited Mead to come there as head of the State Rivers and Water Supply Commission. They offered him six thousand dollars per year, double his government salary. Because he was reluctant to become committed to a job so far from the United States, he decided to go to Australia for only six months. President Wheeler gave him a leave from the university in August 1907, and he agreed to return there as a full-time member of the faculty the following fall. On October 11, the Mead family sailed from Vancouver for Melbourne.[33]

1. *Purdue University, Class of 1882. Elwood Mead is third from left, back row. His diploma bore mention of special work in agriculture and science. (Colorado State University College of Engineering)*

2. *The popular young Professor Mead in his laboratory at Colorado State Agriculture College. (Colorado State University College of Engineering)*

3. *Mead's youthful appearance prompted Francis E. Warren to observe that Mead was "still wearing pinafores" when he came to Wyoming. (Wyoming State Museum)*

4. *Francis E. Warren, Wyoming's first Governor and later a Senator, was a long-time ally of Mead's on reclamation matters. (Wyoming State Museum)*

5. *Representative Frank Mondell of Wyoming. Mead called him "opinionated and somewhat bumptious" at the time of the passage of the Reclamation Act of 1902. (Wyoming State Museum)*

6. *Benjamin Ide Wheeler, President of the University of California at Berkeley from 1899 to 1919. Concerned that his institution was not doing enough for irrigation, Wheeler brought Mead to California. (Bancroft Library, University of California, Berkeley)*

7. *Mead, center, second row, surrounded by the members of the staff of
the Victoria (Australia) State Rivers and Water Supply Commission
in 1912. (Rural Water Commission of Victoria)*

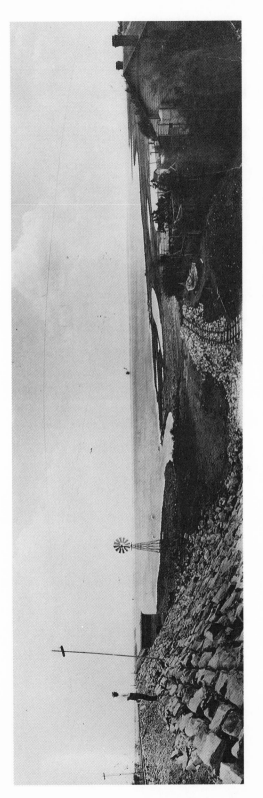

8. *Two views of dam construction in the Waranga Basin north of Melbourne circa 1910. (Rural Water Commission of Victoria)*

9. *Mead with the Superintendents of the two California Land Settlements, Walter E. Packard of Delhi, left, and George Kreutzer of Durham, right. (Bancroft Library, University of California, Berkeley)*

THE DEVELOPMENT OF DVRHAM'S FIRST SETTLER, CARL NEILSEN ~ ALLOTMENT NO. 10, DVRHAM STATE LAND SETTLEMENT, DVRHAM, CALIFORNIA, V.S.A

10. Architect's drawing of the first settlement claimed at the Durham colony, and a view of the actual homestead when completed. (Bancroft Library, University of California, Berkeley)

*11. Farm Laborer Oliver N. Bigcraft and his family in front of their
allotment at Durham. (Bancroft Library, University
of California, Berkeley)*

12. *This portrait of Mead was hung in the main room when the community center at Delhi was dedicated in 1921. When the colony collapsed two years later, angry settlers "lynched it." In searching for photographs for this book, I found a picture of this portrait in the University Archives at Berkeley with a notation on the back that two holes in the oil painting had been repaired. Today it hangs prominently (though not identified) in the entry foyer of Giannini Hall at Berkeley. (Bancroft Library, University of California, Berkeley)*

13. One of these buckets discharged 16 tons of concrete every two minutes for almost two years in the construction of Hoover Dam. (Bureau of Reclamation)

14. Hoover Dam with Lake Mead. (Bureau of Reclamation)

FOUR

■■■■■■■■■

Eight Years "Down Under"

THE MEADS LEFT THE UNITED STATES INTEND-
ing to stay only half a year in Australia. When they arrived in that
nation-continent, however, Dr. Mead found conditions conducive
to testing virtually all of his basic ideas regarding reclamation.
Having united as a Commonwealth only six years earlier, Australians were determined to make theirs a prosperous and populous
nation. In Victoria, government leaders were anxious to do what
was necessary to develop the resources of their state, and a key
aspect of that development was agriculture. Since a key aspect of
Victoria's agriculture was irrigation, Mead had a unique opportunity to promote this type of farming as a basis for the ideal rural
communities he had long envisioned. In addition, he was to play
a key role in solving a long-standing interstate water-rights dispute. The six-month stay eventually turned into an eight-year interlude that Mead later called the most fruitful period of his life.

The Meads reached Melbourne in November 1907. As they
planned for a short stay in Australia, they had stored their house-
hold goods in Washington and intended to have them shipped to
Berkeley as soon as this "season of travel" was finished. Mead had
been asked by the government of the state of Victoria to come
there to advise on its irrigation problems and to help the Commonwealth settle interstate water-rights disputes. Before he would

make long-term commitments, however, he decided first to assess
the situation to see how he could help the government. His initial
impression was quite favorable. The Melbourne newspaper, *The
Age,* greeted Mead enthusiastically, noting that "here at last was
an engineer who could write good English." In a lighter vein, the
paper described a peculiar parallel. The Victoria State Rivers and
Water Supply Commission, which had been established in 1905,
was headed by sixty-eight-year-old Stuart Murray. He had taken
the job temporarily until an ideal candidate could be appointed.
Murray, like Mead, had had an accident that left him with only
one arm. Dr. Mead acknowledged with his usual good humor the
press observation that this was not much of a job apparently since
a man could do it with one hand. The task proved more formidable than that, but the conditions seemed perfect for the American's goals.[1]

In evaluating the conditions, Mead noted that about two-thirds
of Australia was a desert, but only a small area could be irrigated.
This was the Murray-Darling-Murrumbidgee river system located
in the southeast. This drainage basin included parts of the four
states of South Australia, Queensland, New South Wales, and Victoria. Large-scale irrigation had begun a quarter of a century earlier, in the 1880s, when David Syme, the acknowledged "ruler" of
Victoria and editor of *The Age,* Australia's most influential newspaper, became interested in its possibilities. "King David," as he
was often called, arranged to have Alfred Deakin (later prime
minister of Australia) sent to study the latest irrigation methods
in various parts of the world, including America. While in the
United States, he met Mead and discussed water problems and
legislation with him and other experts in the West, and became an
ardent advocate of irrigation. When he returned home, Deakin
helped draft the Irrigation Act of 1886 for Victoria.[2]

The Act of 1886 boldly transferred to the Crown the ownership
of all natural water sources in the state, thus ending the English
inheritance of riparian law. It also provided for the creation of

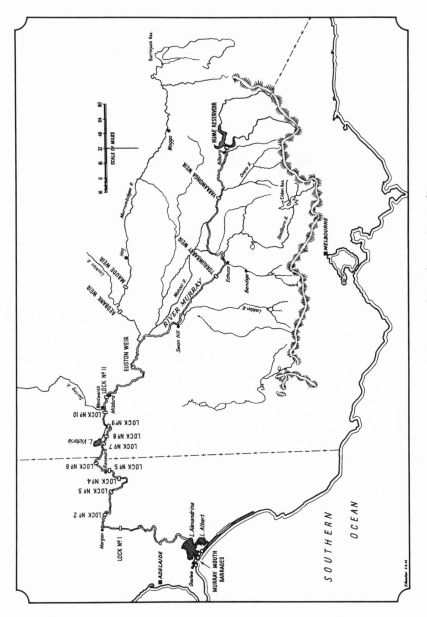

The River Murray of Southeast Australia

local "trusts" to construct irrigation facilities with the aid of state loans, and provided for the government to build some "national works" such as weirs (dams) to serve large areas. For several years it appeared that the most optimistic predictions of reclamation advocates in Victoria would be realized. Dams were built, water was distributed, and the desert began to bloom. A good example of this activity was at Renmark and Mildura on the Murray River, where the American brothers George and William Chaffey constructed several large irrigation projects that prospered until the 1890s. In 1893 the Baring Brothers banking house of London failed, setting off a worldwide depression. Among the casualties in Australia were irrigation projects that were hit especially hard.[3]

As part of the economic revival later in the decade, vigorous attempts were made to promote rural community settlements. Like the agrarian myth in American history, the ideal of the small family farm was a recurring theme "down under." Legislation to attract yeoman farmers had a long and unsuccessful history in Australia, however. In the 1830s, for example, the British government attempted to induce transported convicts who had served their time to take up agriculture, a vocation seen as the key to a virtuous life—and a way to discourage them from returning to the British Isles. Most of these men, however, were attracted to the cities instead. The 1860s saw more attempts, first to deal with the excess miners after the gold rush ended, and a bit later at the behest of railroads seeking freight revenue. Provinces awarded large areas of land to potential farmers, but the results were poor. Much of the land was unsuited to small farming, and few of those who took it had experience in agriculture. An added problem came from rabbits and dingoes (wild dogs). As a result, most of the land ended up in the hands of graziers. For example, in New South Wales, the government doled out twenty-nine million acres from 1861 to 1883, but the cultivated area increased less than half a million acres. Irrigation schemes were then attempted, but they proved successful only on large-scale farms.[4]

In the 1890s, the various provincial governments tried another tack to deal with the latifundia problem and ethos of the pastoral life. To encourage farming, they purchased Crown lands and sold them to colonists on easy terms. Through legislation providing tax incentives and penalties, they hoped to get owners of estates to break up their holdings in a similar manner. As the decade wore on and economic hardships deepened, this idea was further seen as a way to draw the unemployed to the countryside and to lessen the country's dependence on imported (and more expensive) foodstuffs. Like earlier schemes, this idea floundered in a sea of good intentions but poor results as the century ended.[5]

After the formation of the Commonwealth in 1901, increased efforts were undertaken to revive rural life. The world depression had abated, but the government now found new reasons to promote rural development—especially irrigated agriculture. They faced serious obstacles, however. For one thing, the act of union did not resolve a number of conflicts the six provinces had experienced prior to federation; each state clung to as much autonomy as possible. At the constitutional convention, for example, a proposal to give the Commonwealth authority to control navigable streams and their tributaries was defeated because Victoria and New South Wales feared interference with their irrigation projects. Instead, the national government was prohibited from curtailing a state's right to "reasonable use" of river water. This created a controversy that was not resolved until 1915 with an interstate compact Mead was instrumental in putting together. Likewise, immigration policy caused controversy for many years. Because of inequalities of opportunity in the various states, the Commonwealth constitution forbade the use of national funds to assist settlers, lest the rich states be built up at the expense of the poor ones. The urban orientation of the nation and the strength of the Labour party further complicated immigration matters.[6]

Immigration *was* the first major issue that the initial Parliament in 1901 tackled. The legislators adopted a "White Australia" policy to keep out Asians. All immigrants were required to take a dictation test designed to bar persons inimical to the workingman. On the other hand, desirable newcomers were to be encouraged. Farmers, for example, did not affect the labor supply unfavorably, and they not only consumed manufactured goods, but they added to the nation's wealth by producing needed foodstuffs. Accordingly, the state governments passed closer settlements acts to attract farmers to organized rural communities of small farms. Within a few years, these measures appeared headed for the same disappointing results of earlier land schemes until officials in Victoria sought a remedy. At the same time, these leaders began studying another failing farm program: the huge sums of money spent on reclamation projects that were returning few benefits. To help correct this latter problem, they enacted the Victoria Water Act of 1905 that abolished the ninety "trusts" organized since 1886, and placed control of water supplies under the State Rivers and Water Supply Commission.[7]

Little else had been done on these issues by the time Mead arrived in Melbourne to evaluate conditions and consider the chairmanship of the recently established commission. After an initial survey of the situation, Mead submitted his recommendations in January 1908. He claimed that the main obstacle to successful irrigation development in Victoria was the erratic stream flow that varied drastically from year to year. The state needed larger canals and more reservoirs to give a full and assured supply of water. Mead estimated the cost of these works at 20 million dollars, including 7,500,000 dollars for construction of the largest reservoir in the world. When government officials accepted his suggestions and asked him to direct this gigantic project, he wrote to Wheeler requesting a five-year furlough so that he could stay in Australia and supervise the project.[8]

Mead's proposal soon hit a snag that sidetracked most of his plans. The central feature of his project was the Goulburn River. It was located wholly in Victoria, which had invested considerable funds there with poor results. This stream, a tributary of the Murray, was a significant contributor to the total drainage of the vast Murray-Darling-Murrumbidgee watershed. Talk of impeding its flow for irrigation brought immediate protests from officials in both New South Wales and South Australia. They feared the impact of such activity on their states. Victoria could not proceed with significant construction projects until this issue was resolved satisfactorily.[9]

Nevertheless, Mead's position in Australia offered more than engineering opportunities. Besides his suggestions on the technological needs of irrigation in Victoria, he began devising a program to achieve certain social goals desired by officials there. As prosperity returned after the turn of the century, the state government again looked at immigration. Mead saw in this an opportunity to create the agrarian Eden he had envisioned earlier for Wyoming. Two critical factors encouraged him. Because the labor lobby's strength prevented the importation of persons who might jeopardize the industrial workman's status, rural development was the logical area for attention. Moreover, "economic nationalism" dominated the philosophy of the state. Unlike the United States, there was little aversion to state-owned or state-directed enterprises dedicated to the common good. As Mead saw it, the prosperity of Australia could be advanced by peopling its reclaimed desert lands in the interior with immigrant farmers.[10]

In November 1908, after he had become better acquainted with the country and its culture, Mead submitted a comprehensive plan to deal with three significant issues facing Victoria. As he saw it, combining irrigation, immigration, and closer settlement would not only allow the government to salvage money spent on reclamation, but it would also contribute to building the economy. Previously, closer settlement had been restricted to areas watered by rainfall alone. Tying closer settlement to irrigation, he argued, was the only way to justify the expenditure of large sums by the government and to ensure returns commensurate with the finan-

cial outlay. The state should buy up irrigated and irrigable properties in every district, divide them into family-size farms, and assist immigrants with advice and liberal repayment plans until they
became established. The object of irrigation, as Mead saw it, was
not just to produce foodstuffs, but to create the kind of rural en-
vironment that would support a large population of contented
farmers.[11]

A major obstacle to this reordering of the countryside was the
power of the big landowners. As there was only a limited amount
of water for irrigation, it was necessary to obtain maximum efficiency from the available supply. Mead found that the land mag-
nates wasted much of their allotment because of the low charges
for water that had been set in the Water Act of 1905. For example,
large amounts of water were lost by evaporation when transported
long distances; in other places, landowners irrigated grazing lands
or areas with poor soils simply because water was inexpensive.
Mead aroused the enmity of the estate holders by asking for com-
pulsory charges whether the water was used or not. Moreover, he
called for a rate structure set high enough to cover maintenance
and management of the irrigation works, and to help defray construction costs. This should ensure a reliable annual income for
operating expenses and force people to use water properly. Those
owning land would either put it to good use or be forced to sell
their holdings to actual farmers who would.[12]

At Mead's insistence, the State Water Commission bypassed the
ministry and publicized these recommendations, hoping to force
the government into action. This touched off a heated debate,
with most of the big landowners bitterly opposing the plan. Their
position was stated succinctly at one protest meeting, where a
speaker noted that the government had brought sparrows, star-
lings, thistles, and foxes to Australia, but "the greatest pest ever
imported was Dr. Elwood Mead." Nevertheless, in March 1909,
the state legislature passed a bill embodying the Mead proposals.[13]

At this time, officials in Victoria were so pleased with Mead's activities that they raised his salary to ten thousand dollars a year in order to keep him there. With construction of facilities for storage moving forward, albeit slowly, and reforms enacted to make water use more efficient, Mead next turned to the question of attracting colonists. This was the most difficult aspect of his scheme because the government had to do more than sell the reclaimed land. Mead was aware that few potential settlers had money and even fewer had experience in irrigated farming. A method was needed to provide financial assistance and agricultural advice. To help remedy this, the Victoria legislature ordered the State Lands Purchase and Settlement Board, which had been set up in 1904, to cooperate with the Water Commission in irrigation districts. Mead would serve on both bodies in order to facilitate the creation of irrigated closer settlements.[14]

The Settlement Board carefully examined proposed sites for projects and subdivided them into three categories. They designated two-acre plots for subsistence laborers who would learn irrigation farming on their small acreage and earn additional income by seasonal work on larger farms. The board set aside five- to ten-acre allotments for orchards and market gardens, while twenty- to two-hundred-acre tracts were to go to stockmen, dairymen, and regular farmers. A community was thus established. The board also prepared plans for houses and erected them, built fences, and graded the soil so the settler could begin farming as soon as he arrived. Arrangements were made to buy agricultural implements at wholesale prices and to provide continued expert advice on such things as nursery stock, dairy cows, and workhorses. Furthermore, the state government provided loans up to twenty-five hundred dollars at 5 percent interest for improvements. The settler had 15 years to repay these advances, and 21½ years to complete the purchase of his property at 4½ percent interest.[15]

By 1910, most of Mead's suggestions had been adopted and were being implemented. His presence on the Water Commission and the Settlement Board accelerated development of the planned communities. Construction on physical improvements also moved forward, supervised largely by two graduates of Colorado State Agriculture College, Pete Baymeyer and George Kreutzer. Mead brought them down when he discovered that Australia had no engineers trained in irrigation. With these activities proceeding smoothly, the state began an intensified search for qualified persons to put on the land.[16]

In May, Mead led a delegation to Europe and to America to advertise farm opportunities in Victoria and attract settlers. The entourage included Hugh McKenzie, Minister of Lands, and a reporter who covered the trip for the Melbourne newspaper *The Argus*. Italy, their first stop, was something of a fiasco. The Italian government did not want people versed in irrigation to leave, and the Australians did not want anyone without such expertise to come. After a brief examination of their irrigation facilities, the group moved on to the British Isles. There they spent July and August, explaining closer settlement opportunities and advantages in Victoria to prospective settlers. Their task was complicated by agents from other Australian states who were literally giving away undeveloped land. Mead managed a brief and basically fruitless excursion to Denmark before the group sailed to America in September. This phase of the six-month odyssey gave Mead the opportunity to renew old acquaintances, visit his parents in Indiana, and publicize the closer settlement idea in the United States and Canada. Unfortunately, his colonizing efforts proved useless. No settlers from either country responded to the call.[17]

Before Mead returned to Australia in late November, immigrants from England began arriving. *The Argus* reported in October that 301 newcomers entered the state that month, 117 of whom were lured by the closer settlement offer. These were a small part of the general drive to increase immigration that produced nearly a 100,000-person net increase in Australia between 1911 and 1914. Victoria's share of that total was nearly 25 percent, and Mead claimed that about one in three of these were attracted by the closer settlement idea. Not everyone saw it that way. One newspaper compared the publicity techniques of Mead and his cohorts to "a salesman's puffing generalities which most people have learned to discount when not uttered on behalf of governments." Whatever the source of motivation for coming, the immigration population did expand for about three years as did the land under cultivation in closer settlements.[18]

Early in 1911, Mead was riding the crest of popularity and success in Australia. Virtually all of his ideas had been adopted. He seemed to be leading Victoria out of the mire of over a one-thousand-dollar-per-day loss on irrigation. While a few "petifogging critics," as he described them, continued to take swipes at him, he had won over the most influential elements of society. During his first years in Melbourne, he had been torn between the challenges there and the desire to return to California. However, after the 1910 tour abroad to advertise farm advantages in Australia, Mead was buoyed by a new sense of purpose as settlers began filling the land. He pointed with pride to one area with 390 families, where only 12 had lived two years earlier. In another place, a thirty-eight-thousand-acre estate was now occupied by eighty-one homesteads, while in a former "pasture for rabbits," nearly two hundred families were supporting themselves on farms. Every month the arrival of immigrants boosted his reputation. The tone of the letters to his son, Tom, at Berkeley, indicated that he was becoming more entrenched in Australia.[19]

In 1909 Mead had purchased a fourteen-room house in Melbourne for speculative purposes. In the spring of 1911, he decided to move into it and spent five thousand dollars on remodeling. There were now five children at home. Mead had wanted his parents to come and live with them, but his mother died in March 1911 and his father declined to make the trip. A maid, a cook, and a gardener took charge of the domestic chores. In addition, a full-time nurse cared for Katherine, a retarded daughter, injured at birth. A specialist was brought from London to examine her, but nothing could be done. Mead's expenses were over five hundred dollars a month, but he made a good salary and watched his finances carefully. He also did consulting work for the states of Queensland and New South Wales, and invested in a cooperative dairy that added to his income. Besides the gratification he received from his work, Mead's arrangements in Australia provided a comfortable living.[20]

In spite of their pleasant life, the Mead family was plagued with periodic bouts of homesickness. Late in June 1911, the urge to return to America hit hard. Mead sympathized with them, but he said that he intended to serve out his five-year contract. Then his daughter Lucy began thinking about attending college in the United States, and his wife wanted to take Katherine to a specialist in Philadelphia. In October a son, Elwood Lewis, was born, adding to his responsibilities. Financial troubles in America complicated Mead's personal problems further. He had left his business affairs with a friend, George M. Keeney of Rising Sun, Indiana. Keeney disregarded instructions, made several unwise moves, and lost a great deal of money. In April 1912, Mead transferred the management of his investments to Morland B. Binford of Crawfordsville, Indiana.[21]

In the summer of 1912, Mead arranged to come to the United States, ostensibly to secure settlers, but also to straighten out his finances. While in California, he sounded out Dr. Wheeler about returning to the university, and the president promised to see what he could do. After his return to Melbourne, Mead pressed Wheeler about a job and was informed in January 1913 that there were no positions available at that time. Mead resigned himself to "end his days" in Australia. He believed he had "reached the age when one begins to think of ceasing all work rather than beginning anew."[22]

Back in Australia, Mead immersed himself in his work. As immigrants continued to arrive and new settlements were developed, the task of overseeing thirty projects in Victoria meant long hours and a great deal of traveling. Yet Mead was happy because here at last he could demonstrate the social and economic benefits of irrigation that he had so long touted. He got additional satisfaction from his leadership role in putting together an agreement to settle the thorny problem of appropriating the waters of the Murray River system.[23]

As noted earlier, a major controversy thwarted the full development of irrigation potentialities in Australia. This was the division of the only major watershed on the continent, the Murray River and its tributaries. These streams cut across the southeastern corner of Australia, draining mainly the two states of New South Wales and Victoria, before exiting to the sea through the state of South Australia. The dispute centered on the determination of New South Wales and Victoria to use these waters for irrigation and South Australia's objection because of the impact this would have on the navigability of the river. The issue was broached first in the 1850s, but the primitive state of irrigation and the importance of the river as an artery of commerce overshadowed the need for a solution at that time. By the 1880s, however, the age of irrigation and the extension of railroads to the interior drastically altered the situation. Nevertheless, South Australia remained implacable and the dilemma dragged on into the twentieth century.[24]

In 1902 a severe drought brought the dispute into focus again. The dry spell caused the flow of the watershed to drop from an average drainage of 9.3 million acre feet to 2.3 million acre feet that year. This drop was disastrous for the numerous irrigators in Victoria and New South Wales and demonstrated the need for major reservoirs to store and regulate the runoff of the various streams. At the same time, the low flow proved to officials in South Australia how development of the river could make the Murray virtually unusable for boat traffic and expose its mouth to an influx of damaging salt water at high tide. The situation crystalized the position of both sides and, at the same time, compelled compromise. Experts now agreed that the river system had to be developed as a unit. One of the reasons Mead had been hired was to help resolve this conflict.[25]

Negotiations were conducted by correspondence until 1909, when leaders in Victoria pushed for the creation of a royal commission. Mead played a key role in this body and skillfully molded an accord. By 1913 negotiators resolved the basic issues of the dispute. Two years later, after the fine points were ironed out, the Murray River Agreement was signed. This pact set up a commission of representatives of the Commonwealth and each of the three states. In dividing the waters, Victoria and New South Wales each got two-fifths and South Australia one-fifth of the total. Furthermore, a series of locks were to be constructed to assure the navigability of the Murray, and a locking system would be built at its mouth to prevent saltwater damage. The cost of these facilities would be shared equally by the four contracting parties (The Commonwealth would pay one-fourth as well). Ironically, the pact paved the way to complete the recommendations Mead had made in 1908 just as he was making plans to return to America.[26]

As these developments were unfolding, officials at Berkeley contacted Mead in June 1913 about a position in the Agriculture College. He wanted to accept, but vacillated when he was actually faced with the prospect of leaving Australia. After he was formally offered the position of Professor of Rural Institutions in August, he submitted his resignation to the premier of Victoria. Mead wrote to his son, Tom, that it "was accepted so quick that [he] felt humiliated and . . . decided to leave on the October boat." He cabled President Wheeler of his plans. In the meantime, news of his leaving leaked out and "settlers, businessmen, and everyone from janitor up" pressured the government to retain the engineer. *The Age* carried a long editorial reviewing and lauding Mead's accomplishments. The writer lamented that Mead had seen the tree planted and watered, but he would not be there when the fruit was gathered. This ground swell of support caused Mead to change his mind. He felt he should show that he appreciated the regard accorded to him. He wired the university for permission to delay his arrival until the end of the irrigation season in May 1914, but he confided to Tom that he was inclined to stay in Melbourne for another five years.[27]

Mead now had agreements with two places. In February 1914, Victoria officials arranged for him to travel to America to study recent developments in irrigation—and to straighten out his commitments. At Berkeley, Wheeler urged Mead to rejoin the faculty, and agreed to let him return to Australia annually for two or three months. On reflection, this appeared to be an unworkable arrangement and was dropped. Mead was also approached by Secretary of the Interior Franklin K. Lane about taking the directorship of the Reclamation Service. Lane wanted to replace Frederick H. Newell, who was under attack from the water users. Mead gave some thought to the offer, but decided that he did not want to revive that old bitterness. After visiting friends at the university and in the federal government, Mead sailed for Melbourne with plans to stay for at least another year.[28]

During the spring and summer of 1914, a severe drought returned to Australia. The Murray discharge was 1.9 million acre feet that year (400,000 feet less than in 1902) and the salinity content rose to disastrous proportions, once again heightening the need for major storage facilities. This problem, combined with discontented settlers, "many of whom will neither pay up nor get out," made those months the hardest Mead had faced in Australia. He felt the strain but persevered because he believed himself to be needed. In September, the University of California tendered him a new offer at a better salary than proposed earlier. Meanwhile, World War I had begun and this created uncertainties about the future of the Australian planned settlements and Mead's own presence there. Immigration had started to taper off early in 1914, and it ceased altogether with the outbreak of hostilities. Mead feared that it would be a long conflict and that funds to continue his programs would be drastically curtailed, if not stopped, until the war was over.[29]

By year's end, Mead again was giving serious thought to teaching at Berkeley. He was uneasy over the war, and the increasingly hostile attitude of Australians toward American neutrality made him fear that this would affect his relations with the government. Moreover, there were increasing problems with disgruntled settlers. A significant number by this time had run out of money and credit and were not yet the beneficiaries of the higher prices that the war was to bring. These were the first signs of flaws in Mead's closer settlement schemes. In April 1915, Mead tendered his resignation to Victoria officials, effective as soon as the irrigation season ended. In May, the Mead family sailed for San Francisco.[30]

Mead's departure was genuinely regretted by most of the people with whom he worked in Australia. They appreciated what they regarded as important and lasting contributions to the development of that continent-country. In letter after letter, settlers expressed their appreciation for his efforts in their behalf. He knew many of them personally and had always shown an interest in their welfare on his numerous tours of the countryside. In 1915, a Royal Commission investigating closer settlement noted that Mead had solved a great problem in Victoria "where previous attempts . . . had been ignominious in their failure." The Minister of Water Supply called him "an enthusiast, and it was only an enthusiast who could have got irrigation started at all." In specific and tangible terms, Mead had overseen the division of some 100,000 acres into closer settlements, had significantly advanced the dairy works as well as the dried and canned food industries, and had brought the major irrigation efforts of Victoria to solvency. Government officials lamented his leaving, and presented him with a silver boomerang surmounted with a gold kangaroo.[31]

Not everyone shared these sentiments, of course. In fact, the flaws in Mead's policies were already apparent. As early as 1914, another severely dry year, some of the first immigrants under his closer settlement scheme ran out of money and complained that they had been deceived or misled. Others, lured to Australia by the attraction of land, abandoned the countryside for the city where jobs and higher wages, by-products of World War I, beckoned. For those who stayed, wartime demands for agricultural products brought higher prices and temporary prosperity. However, the return to "normalcy" in the early 1920s brought renewed farm problems "down under." [32]

Mead called his years in Victoria the "most fruitful experience" of his life. It taught him the importance of teamwork and demonstrated the validity of the ideas on irrigation that he had been preaching for many years. He had become quite imbued with the Australian attitude toward government paternalism during his stay. In an article in *The Independent* in 1911, he had written that the great lesson for America was that Australians "have learned that they can act wisely and efficiently in carrying out great works for the common good . . . and it is the welfare of the many rather than the enrichment of the few, which is the governing principle." By the time he left Victoria, these sentiments had become much stronger. In 1915, he told the Royal Commission on Closer Settlement that the "individual cannot be considered in a matter of national development. The individual must give way in the interest of the state." Shortly thereafter, Mead left Australia convinced that the United States was behind the rest of the world in industrial and social legislation. [33]

FIVE

World War I Work

MEAD RETURNED TO THE UNITED STATES IN 1915, enthusiastic over his success in Australia and anxious to establish planned settlements in his native country. Since his visit in 1914, he had been disseminating information on closer settlement and rural credits in Australia to various persons throughout the nation. He was quite optimistic that his ideas would be accepted here because so many people in America seemed interested in them. In fact, he had been lured back to the University of California by officials there who were especially concerned about the condition of agriculture in their state. But before he could direct his full attention to their concerns, leaders in Washington, D.C. sought his advice. For the next five years Mead was to devote half of his time to advising on national problems of reclamation and settlement. Beginning in 1917, most of this work related to World War I and its aftermath.[1]

In January 1915, after Mead had accepted the position at Berkeley, Secretary of the Interior Franklin K. Lane wrote to him in Australia seeking his assistance. Lane asked Mead to serve as chairman of a Central Board of Cost Review that was being set up to investigate financial charges on federal reclamation projects. The Newlands Act, which had been in operation for thirteen years, was being severely criticized by water users. In particular, they were upset over the high construction charges they were assessed. In 1914 the government doubled the length of time for repayment from ten to twenty years, and made provision for graduated payments, but this had not stilled dissent. Early in 1915 Lane called for a thorough review of project costs and a revision of repayments where they were justified.[2]

Mead agreed to accept the chairmanship after it was arranged that headquarters for the Central Board would be at Berkeley, so that this work would not interfere with his teaching duties at the university. Two other men, General William L. Marshall, consulting engineer to the secretary of the interior, and Ignatius D. O'Donnell, supervisor of irrigation for the Reclamation Service, served with Mead on the board. They were to evaluate and make recommendations based on the findings of local boards set up on each of the federal reclamation projects in the West.[3]

The recommendations of Mead's Central Review Board proved disappointing to the water users. They had expected that the inquiries would mean a significant lowering of the charges they had to repay the government for construction costs. Their optimism increased when the report of the first local board to complete its work, the Carlsbad, New Mexico, irrigation project, was published in June 1915. Before these findings were submitted to Lane, or examined by Mead's Central Board, they were released to the press and widely distributed in other reclamation-project areas.[4]

The Carlsbad project was perhaps the worst reclamation scheme the federal government had tackled. Begun as a private irrigation enterprise in 1887, the project suffered constant financial difficulties and was on the verge of ruin when the Reclamation Service took it over in 1904. Federal estimates initially called for the expenditure of 450,000 dollars, but this figure more than doubled by the time work was completed in 1912. The water users had agreed to pay thirty-one dollars per acre for construction costs, but when additional work was necessary they voluntarily assented in 1911 to an increase in the charge to forty-five dollars an acre. By 1915 they decided that this was too high, and the local board of review confirmed their objections. That board issued its report with two recommendations: one set the charge at $34.00 an acre, the other at $20.71.[5]

When the Central Review Board studied the Carlsbad report, the members rejected the local body's findings. Instead of approving a reduction in charges, they raised the repayment rate to forty-seven dollars an acre. Mead's group expressed sympathy for the "small number of water users" who were having a hard time, but observed that their plight was not due to high water charges or construction costs. The evils of the project were "inflated land prices, high freight charges, high interest rates, alien landlordism, [and] a nominal and not actual compliance with the regulations fixing the size of farm units that closely verges on fraud." Any reduction, they contended, would "simply go into the pockets of the present speculative owners or increase the value of any mortgage on these lands, or both." Unfortunately, the conclusions of the Central Board concerning the Carlsbad project applied to most of the ventures of the federal government in reclamation.[6]

As the local boards examined the individual projects, they were limited in what they could do. Almost everywhere the construction costs had exceeded original estimates, the number of acres to be reclaimed fell short of expectations, and crop yields and prices were disappointing. Nevertheless, the contracts called for repayment by the water users. After evaluating the data, the board made minor alterations by disallowing questionable expenses and modifying total acreages. Further reductions resulted from the 1914 Act, which called for eliminating expenses connected with the Washington, D.C., headquarters. The total decrease, unfortunately, was more symbolic than substantial. Relief—albeit of a temporary nature—came in the form of greater demand and higher prices for agricultural products due to World War I.[7]

In July 1915, while the inquiry was still in process, and after six projects had been investigated, Mead wrote to Interior Secretary

Lane, suggesting changes in the Reclamation Act. In five of the cases studied, the land was mainly in private hands when the government began its construction program, he noted; and the improvements had increased values from four to tenfold. Excessive prices charged to settlers for this land, however, tended to absorb the benefits of the government's expenditures. This situation could be traced largely to speculators who were now "among the most active in urging that a large part of the cost be written off." Mead's solution was to fix the price on the land to be sold before irrigation works were started.[8]

Mead further suggested that interest be included in cost repayments. The lack of interest charges amounted to a donation to wealthy landowners and speculators, he said. Besides, it made settlers of modest means "feel that they are the objects of special privilege; it whets the appetite for further concessions; it has in it the seeds of repudiation." Finally, Mead asked for active government participation in assisting settlers on both publicly and privately owned reclamation projects. Most of the good acreage was in private hands, he conceded, but these owners would not or could not afford to give aid to settlers. Without government help the projects could not succeed. He cautioned that aid be extended in a way that "those directly benefited shall pay the whole cost" and "the well-to-do shall not absorb the benefits and the poor settlers shoulder the burden."[9]

In his reply to Mead, Secretary Lane called attention to the fact that the act that had extended the payment period to twenty years also provided that the government may fix a maximum price on privately owned lands within future projects. Likewise, while it was true that contracts already made did not call for interest, he agreed with Mead that "this principle should be adopted [on] any new works." As to financial aid in settlement, the secretary expressed interest in the idea and hoped that a rural credits bill slated for introduction in the next session of Congress would provide for it.[10]

Mead's interest—at this point almost an obsession—went beyond altering deficiencies in the Reclamation Act. He wanted to set up a national "demonstration area" to test the feasibility and show the value of a scheme similar to the Australian system. In June 1915 he discussed plans for this with Lane in Washington, and the following month he wrote the secretary that he had found an ideal spot on the Wind River in Wyoming for the experiment. In this letter, Mead stressed another conviction—the importance of interest on amortized charges for land, construction, or improvements. He pointed out that interest would disarm opponents by showing that the demonstration project would not cost taxpayers anything. It would also remove criticism from older settlers who had not been aided in improving their farms. Since this proposal required congressional approval, Mead urged Lane to push the idea and become "the pioneer" in introducing planned settlements in America.[11]

Initially, Mead hoped to found one model planned settlement to demonstrate the possibilities of rural life. He believed that if he could create such a community in the United States—as he had done on numerous projects in Australia—it would serve as a pattern for revitalizing American agriculture. The best starting place for land reform, he insisted, was a reclamation project where an entirely new area could be developed. The expertise that went into the engineering aspects of irrigation would be extended to include economic, agricultural, and social planning. All the needs of those who took up land there would be fulfilled; farms would be grouped around a village with stores, church, school, cooperative markets, and a recreational center.[12]

Mead was not the only person concerned about rural life in America. The early years of the twentieth century—the Progressive Era—coincided with a back-to-nature movement that reflected discontent with the trends in society. Whether its wellsprings were the closing of the frontier or a revulsion toward urban life and bigness in industry, significant numbers of people looked to an idealized agrarian past. Mead's approach centered on creating new farm opportunities through reclamation or reordering the countryside with farm-and-factory communities that combined the best of the past and the present.[13]

Other people saw planned communities as a way to create opportunities for the unemployed. In 1915, Secretary of Labor William B. Wilson proposed some such scheme to cut down the number of persons out of work. He believed that the government should launch new programs to provide benefits previously available through the Homestead Act and the frontier functioning as a safety valve. A colonization bill that called for the expenditure of fifty million dollars was introduced in 1916. Mead helped draft the legislation and testified before the Labor Committee on its behalf, but it was never reported out of committee. When several lawmakers asked him to draft another proposal, he once again wrote to Lane. He saw this as a "growing recognition of the need for something different—an opportunity to begin the greatest agrarian reform of a century, and I should like to see you recognized as the one who put it through." However, before anything more could be done, America entered World War I and domestic issues were temporarily shelved.[14]

Besides affording a respite to settlers on projects, the European conflict raised the specter of increased activity for the Reclamation Service. Rising prices and an expanding demand for farm goods gave the marginal farmer new hope for success; in fact, the food shortages led to a concerted government campaign to increase agricultural production. Reclaimed land was a logical target for such efforts. In 1917, Herbert Hoover, head of the Food Administration, called Mead to Washington to assist with this aspect of the war effort. Hoover told University of California President Wheeler that it seemed "almost imperative that the Food Administration should have his [Mead's] assistance and counsel in helping solve some of the problems coming before it." The California professor's chief assignment was to help arrange for "harmonious and efficient cooperation" between the States Relation Service of the Agriculture Department and the Reclamation Service of the Department of the Interior. This was no easy task. Friction between the two departments in the area of reclamation dated back at least to the Newell–Mead conflict in the 1890s. World War I perhaps quieted, but did not end, the rivalry.[15]

The war clearly offered the Reclamation Service an excuse to expand its operations. The agency started two new projects in 1917, and Mead pushed plans to complete the facilities to irrigate undeveloped lands on projects already operational. He spent most of his time, however, in visiting the twenty-four reclamation projects scattered throughout the West, consulting with local officials on production problems, and advising on the best crops to plant. When the opportunity presented itself, he backed innovative ideas to boost agricultural output. For example, University of Nevada students planned to farm a one-thousand-acre tract of land on the Truckee–Carson project to help increase food production. Mead was enthusiastic and urged Arthur Powell Davis, director of the Reclamation Service, to cooperate. Davis agreed to level the land and postpone payments for the water until the crops were harvested. But he noted that his agency had no funds for seed, agricultural equipment, or labor costs. As private capital would have to finance these aspects of the scheme, the idea was abandoned. Nonetheless, Mead was encouraged by the willingness of government officials to consider assistance, and he was buoyed by the publicity the proposal engendered.[16]

Although government help for the Truckee–Carson scheme was advanced as a wartime measure, Mead believed that the government should provide more than water to projects as a matter of course. Earlier, he had convinced Franklin Lane of the efficacy of the idea and the secretary recommended an appropriation of two million dollars to put unused reclamation land into production in 1917. Agriculture Department officials blocked the plan. They not only objected to another department going into farming, but they questioned whether such an activity was a "desirable one for any branch of the Government." In the main, their protests against the funding were well taken. Several years would elapse before reclaimed areas would produce sizable quantities of crops, and meanwhile the manpower needed to prepare the land would add to the serious wartime farm-labor shortage. They anticipated that the war would be over before benefits would begin. Agriculture's departmental chauvinism and rivalry with the Interior Department also played a part. As one official put it, "When the Interior Department gets ready to go into farming, it will do so if we do not beat them to it."[17]

While the cry of wartime necessity did not give the Reclamation Service the excuse to expand its functions, the increased demand for foodstuffs, with its attendant rise in prices, not only provided support to those who advocated extending cultivated areas, but it also made farming economically attractive once again. This, in turn, aided Mead in his struggle to have his colonization scheme tried; irrigated farms were proving to be a financial success. What better way, therefore, to reward the doughboy, who was sacrificing his share of the war's prosperity "over there," than to provide a farm for him when he returned?

In July 1918, Secretary Lane requested that Mead's leave from the University of California be extended so that he could assist with postwar reconstruction. Lane had been attracted to Mead's plan for organized land settlement before the war, and now he sought his expertise in promoting farms for returning soldiers. The California professor had been collecting information on the subject since March, and Lane wanted him to stay in Washington until legislation to implement the plan could be passed. In May, Lane had written to Woodrow Wilson proposing such a scheme and had received his endorsement. Various bills along the lines sketched in Lane's letter to the president were placed before Congress.[18]

The most important bill among those sent to Congress embodied Mead's ideas and was written essentially by him. Representative Frank Mondell, his old Wyoming colleague, introduced it. The proposed legislation called for an appropriation of 500 million dollars to develop projects of family-size farms in each state. To broaden its political appeal, the act called for the reclaiming of swamp, cutover, and abandoned areas, in addition to the arid lands of the West. The soldier would make a down payment of 5 percent, and the remainder would be financed by the government over a forty-year period. In order to avoid the opprobrium of a federal giveaway, interest would be charged. Finally, to provide employment during the reconversion period after the war, the government would hire ex-servicemen to prepare the sites for cultivation.[19]

Mead faced a difficult task in convincing legislators of the Mondell bill's merits as well as interesting servicemen in the scheme. Almost everyone agreed on the desirability of rewarding the returning men, but the form it should take was another matter. To many legislators, the Mondell proposal was attractive because of its association with the agrarian ideal and past veteran bonuses of land—and because it was the least expensive among the propositions put forward. Initial support was broadly based. It included "back-to-the-landers"; national leaders; business, veteran, and labor groups; and people in those areas most likely to benefit— the West and the South. The Reclamation Service pushed the plan and, as part of a propaganda campaign, published a survey Mead conducted on soldier settlement schemes in other English-speaking countries.[20]

On the other hand, almost everyone connected with farming—from Secretary of Agriculture David F. Houston down to the lowliest farmer—denounced the plan. Their objections varied, but in the main, criticism centered on the fear of postwar overproduction and low prices. They were soon joined by the American Legion. After studying the proposal, the Legion's directors denounced the plan, noting that it really gave soldiers nothing except preference in their application.[21]

Before opposition coalesced, however, backers of the program united with Mead in a vigorous campaign of support. They put special importance on contacting servicemen and convincing them to back the bill. Mead arranged to have his California assistant Frank Adams go to France after the Armistice as part of the Army Education Corps to talk up farm opportunities for veterans. Mead had planned to go, but other duties prevented him from making the trip. Instead, he traveled extensively in this country promoting the scheme. The Interior Department distributed among the troops 900,000 copies of *Hey There! Do You Want a Home on the Farm?*, a booklet with a return postcard, and received 140,000 replies. The result of these efforts had little effect on lawmakers in Washington, however. By the time the veteran-farm measures emerged from committee, the war was over and peace negotiations had come and gone. Enthusiasm for rewarding the soldiers waned once the guns were silenced. Other issues—the Red Scare, strikes, the battle over the Treaty of Versailles, and the election of 1920—came to the fore. America moved toward "normalcy"—the continued industrialization and urbanization of the nation. The idea of rejuvenating the countryside with model communities of ex-servicemen was not part of the postwar scheme.[22]

Mead and the other leaders of the movement for soldier settlements were not easily dissuaded by the declining sentiment for their plan. Although he ended his full-time service with the Interior Department in April 1919, Mead continued to promote his scheme and urge support for it. The apparent success of the state settlement established under his direction in 1918 at Durham, California, aided his cause. In 1920, Mead wrote *Helping Men Own Farms*, which painted a glowing picture of colonization in Australia and in Durham. Despite these efforts and those of other backers, however, no federal legislation was enacted. Bills were debated in committee, and one even passed the House of Representatives in 1920, but the only settlement measure to reach the White House was contained in a bonus bill that President Warren G. Harding vetoed in 1921.[23]

Thus ended, for a while at least, Mead's vision of a national reordering of the countryside. He had spent almost half of his time between 1915 and 1919 working for the federal government, and it had been a valuable experience. Through his position on the Cost Review Board, he became thoroughly conversant with the current condition of reclamation in the West. This enabled him to point out its defects, and it gave him a platform to publicize the lessons he had learned in Australia. Mead was disappointed but not discouraged that none of his ideas had come to fruition either before the war or in connection with the soldier-settlement scheme. His efforts for the next four years would be devoted mainly to his duties at Berkeley and to land settlement in California.

SIX

Durham and Delhi

WHILE HIS IDEAS ON FARM COLONIES FAILED
to gain support in Congress, Mead convinced the California legislature to try the experiment. In presenting his program, the cele-
brated engineer drew on his international reputation as an expert
on irrigation and settlement, and secured the backing of many
influential persons concerned with the condition of rural life. The
state lawmakers set up a Land Settlement Board with Mead as its
chairman, and appropriated funds in 1917 and 1919 to establish
demonstration communities at Durham and Delhi in northern
California. Mead directed this endeavor for six years while teaching at the University of California. He had hoped that the colonies would be examples for a reordering of the countryside, but
unfortunately they were beset by serious problems and eventually
failed.

Mead's reappointment at Berkeley in 1915 had been arranged by
people interested in improving the condition of rural life in California, including President Wheeler. Because B. A. Etcheverry had
replaced Mead as head of the Irrigation Department, Wheeler established a new position—Professor of Rural Institutions—for
Mead and gave him a free hand to do what he wanted in his field.
The appointment was ideal. Mead's interests ranged over a broad
scope of agrarian issues—from sowing to selling, from the educa-

tion of farmers to their social life. His principal goal, of course, was the introduction of the Australian plan of settlement into the United States.[1]

Mead's first step toward securing legislation for his land-settlement idea was to demonstrate a need for change. While visiting the United States in 1914, he had found Governor Hiram V. Johnson receptive to the Australian scheme. The next year, however, Johnson would not support legislation to issue bonds for land colonization because he claimed it might jeopardize another bond issue he deemed essential, but more importantly because he wanted a study made before he committed himself. To this end, the legislature established a State Commission on Colonization and Rural Credits in 1915. Several prominent Californians served on the panel, including Chester Rowell, Harris Weinstock, Mortimer Fleishhacker, and Dean David P. Barrows. Mead was chairman. In February 1916, the prestigious Commonwealth Club of San Francisco voted one thousand dollars to aid in research. Soon thereafter, a cooperative investigation was launched by a group composed of Mead, representing the state commission; Frank Adams, acting for the club; and D. N. Morgan of the university's College of Agriculture, serving as secretary.[2]

Under Mead's direction, the group made an extensive survey in 1916 to determine the nature and condition of thirty-two private land-settlement schemes in California. Practically everyone connected with agriculture and irrigation in the state assisted in gathering information: county agents, agriculture college faculties, managers of the private colonies, rural bank officials, actual settlers, and Mead's students. They conducted thousands of individual interviews and elicited an equal number of written statements. The bulk of their information came from settlers on the state's thirty-two private colonies. These farmers answered questionnaires describing the size of their farms, capital at the time of purchase, purchase price, terms of sale, improvements before and since purchase, acreage under cultivation, stock census, and indebtedness. In addition, respondents were invited to make specific remarks about their condition. The investigators drew up summary conclusions for each colony.[3]

Not surprisingly the composite picture that emerged from this survey confirmed what Mead contended—there was a definite need for reform in colonization practices, and indeed in rural life in California. The survey painted a black picture. Many farmers took the opportunity to air pent-up grievances and blamed their misfortunes on the land companies; some charged misrepresentation and others outright fraud. The individual reports on the private schemes, while noting the existence of unscrupulous private enterprises, did not indict the land companies as such, however. Rather, they pointed to the defects in the land-colonization system itself. The basic problem, the group concluded, was that private companies focused on developing and selling land for profit, not on social planning or job training; they did little to assist the settler. This was not because companies wished to trick people into buying and then leave them stranded, but because they did not understand what the farmer needed to begin successful operations, nor did they have the funds to help him.[4]

Mead's commission drew up a comprehensive plan to deal with these problems. The centerpiece was a "state demonstration in scientific colonization," which Mead insisted was not an experiment because it followed the same policy successfully pursued in Australia. The project would show land companies a program that would benefit both developer and settler. According to the proposal, which was submitted to Governor Johnson in 1916, California would purchase a ten-thousand-acre tract selected by a special committee. This land would be divided into two hundred regular farms varying in size from twenty to one hundred acres, depending on the quality of the soil and the crops to be grown. There would also be one hundred two-acre farm labor plots and three hundred acres for schools, public buildings, and a townsite.[5]

After the site had been selected and subdivided, the land would

be prepared for cultivation. The land would be leveled and irrigation ditches built. (Mead believed an irrigated area essential for
closer settlement because a farmer could grow a specialized crop
on a small acreage.) The project then would be opened for inspection and applications accepted from prospective farmers. A board
would select the settlers, a process designed to weed out potential
failures. If a person lacked sufficient capital or experience for farming, he was to be offered a two-acre laborers' plot. The smaller
allotments would provide the additional manpower needed for
seasonal shortages on larger farms and enable the laborer to acquire the necessary skill or cash to advance to a regular farm.[6]

Mead designed the credit arrangements to correct financing
problems revealed in the commission's report. According to its
findings, land companies generally sold at one-fourth or one-third
down, with 5.8 years the average time allowed for payment in full,
and 6.9 percent the average contract rate of interest. As a result,
the farmer usually expended his capital getting started, then had
to borrow—if he could—to purchase equipment and meet a high
repayment schedule while trying to overcome the formidable obstacles of making virgin land productive. Mead proposed an initial
cash outlay of 5 percent, with interest at 4½ percent and amortized
annual payments on the principal of 1½ percent beginning at the
end of the fourth year. Repayment would take thirty-six years, but
the farmer would have funds to buy his equipment and pay for
state-constructed dwellings, outbuildings, and fences, all of which
would be completed by the time he took possession.[7]

The Mead scheme went beyond this, however, and provided
additional and continuing benefits to the colonizer. "A single competent superintendent" would direct operations, collect payments,
give advice on farm management and cultivation, and aid in buying livestock and equipment. Mead saw the advisor as a key ele-
ment of the plan. His role, similar to the overseer in Australia,
would be to monitor the progress of the settler, give him advice,
and if he did not heed it, report him to the authorities who con-

trolled loans or extensions of payments. Moreover, each colony would organize a cooperative to purchase and sell goods, giving members the financial advantage of group bargaining. Finally, closer settlements would transform the social life of rural areas by ending the isolation of the country and bringing people together in a community.[8]

In the fall of 1916, when Governor Johnson received the report, Commission member Harris Weinstock asked him to "father" the plan and present it to the legislature as "your child." If the act passed, he said, it would be "the crowning glory of your very remarkable gubernatorial record." Mead gave impetus to the plan, claiming it would serve as a model for developing millions of additional acres of arable, irrigable California land, attracting up to 350,000 newcomers to the state. A bill embodying the general scheme was drafted in January 1917, and the governor agreed to support it. Sharp opposition arose immediately from real estate men. They called it an attack on meritorious land agents and private colonization companies, and denounced it as governmental intrusion into business. The popular *Sunset Magazine,* on the other hand, favored the plan, as did a majority of the lawmakers in the California assembly. The legislature enacted a bill which set up a Land Settlement Board and appropriated 260,000 dollars to start a demonstration project.[9]

Dr. Mead was named chairman of the Land Settlement Board and immediately began to put the plan in operation. Although he was still working for Herbert Hoover in connection with the war effort, he visited California regularly to direct the undertakings. Mead possessed outstanding organizational skills and surrounded himself with subordinates in whom he had complete trust. Early in 1918, he oversaw the purchase of a 6,239-acre track of land near Durham in the middle of the Sacramento Valley. George C. Kreutzer, who had gone to Australia in 1908 and directed a closer settlement under Mead there, was named superintendent of the proposed colony. He was a close personal friend and thoroughly understood the methods and objectives of his mentor. A personable individual who inspired confidence among those around him, Kreutzer also had an excellent business sense.[10]

Arranging the finances for the Durham colony tested Mead's ingenuity. The 260,000 dollars allotted by the legislature was not sufficient to purchase land and construct a settlement of the size he envisioned. The land alone cost almost 550,000 dollars, of which some 200,000 dollars was paid in cash. This left about 50,000 dollars to make the necessary improvements. To supplement this, an association of the earliest-selected settlers obtained a loan of nearly 100,000 dollars from the Federal Land Bank and turned the money over to the board. With this cash, construction of the ditches began and a work force contoured the surface. The College of Agriculture at Berkeley, meanwhile, made surveys and classified the soil. On the basis of these reports, Mead subdivided the project into 110 farms, varying in size from eight to three hundred acres, and 26 two-acre allotments for farm laborers. The property had cost an average of 80 dollars an acre, and was sold for 150 dollars an acre with prices ranging from 48 dollars to 300 dollars per acre.[11]

The board opened the first unit of land in May 1918 and the remainder in November. With over one thousand people applying, the 110 farms were sold immediately; there were six applicants for each farm-laborer allotment. Mead's board carefully screened the prospective settlers. The basic criteria required an applicant to have agricultural experience and between 1,500 dollars and 2,500 dollars in cash, depending on the size of the farm to be purchased. Every person selected had farm experience and easily met the financial requirements, with an average initial capital of 6,232 dollars. The other group—the farm laborers—came to Durham with an average net worth of 789 dollars.[12]

When these settlers and their families took up residence, the project resembled an established farm community. The land had been prepared—much of it was seeded for pasture—and most of the homes were ready for occupancy. Housing, in fact, was an important aspect of the planned development. Mead had obtained an architect from the state engineer's office to draw up a number of house blueprints designed to meet the needs and financial capabilities of the settlers. The dwellings, which varied in price from 800 dollars to 1,500 dollars, were constructed of material purchased in wholesale lots, offering additional savings. When a person signed a contract for a farm, he selected a design and the house was completed by the time he moved onto his land. A 40 percent down payment was required on a home in order to secure a state loan, and no allotment could be sold or sublet until the land was paid in full. Hence, both the settler and the state had a sizable investment in the future of the project.[13]

As an additional stimulus to success, Mead and Kreutzer encouraged team work among the settlers. Cooperatives purchased farm equipment and seeds in wholesale lots, and built cold-storage facilities for goods used for personal consumption. Since a majority of the farmers took up dairying, the most important cooperative was the Stock Breeders' Association. To ensure uniformly high-quality animals at the lowest possible cost, this group established a committee which, with the help of an expert, selected herds in other parts of California. They brought the cattle to Durham, where they were sold to the individual farmers. This association also constructed a central milk station to process and sell the dairy products, giving the settler an advantage when marketing goods as well.[14]

Initially, the Durham colony seemed to be healthy, although certain unusual factors distorted that appearance. While it was true that up to January 1, 1920, the settlers had met all of their payments to the state on schedule, most had used capital they brought with them to pay part of those obligations. Then, too, farm prices were inflated in 1918 and 1919 due to the war. Moreover, the Settlement Board had been able to select persons with almost ideal qualifications because of the large number of applicants. The consequences of these facts was yet to be felt. In the meantime, the project served as a model to push for funds to open another settlement. Mead's plan to secure national legislation to provide farms for soldiers was not going well. In California, however, he could point to Durham, with its contented colonists, and plead for similar settlements as a bonus for returning veterans.[15]

In 1919 the California legislature passed a second settlement bill, with the same provisions as the 1917 Act, except that it established a 1-million-dollar revolving fund for this venture (125,000 dollars was diverted to Durham) and provided preference for war veterans. Mead stressed the veteran bonus aspect in promoting the legislation, but a reward for soldiers did not prove out in practice. The Settlement Board soon found itself embroiled in a dispute with the American Legion, which pointed out that preference meant little because Mead insisted that the qualifications of experience and a minimum of fifteen hundred dollars in cash could not be lowered without jeopardizing the success of the program. The Legion called the whole thing a farce, noting that if a soldier were fortunate enough to have the capital required he would not need to enter a state colony. Then too, they pointedly noted, funds allotted were only enough to develop one settlement, hardly a munificent gesture of gratitude to the tens of thousands of California men who served in the war.[16]

As a site for the second settlement, Mead's board chose an 8,400-acre tract of land near Delhi in Merced County, at the northern end of the San Joaquin Valley. They paid approximately 800,000 dollars for it, with the bulk going to one Edgar M. Wilson. Many considered this to be an inflated price for the property. For example, one member of the board, Judge William H. Langdon, who had been reared in that area, warned Mead that the tract was known as one "over which the jack rabbits carried their lunches when they crossed it." Nevertheless, Mead persuaded his colleagues to buy the site at an average cost of ninety-six dollars an acre. The land required a great deal of leveling and the installation of an extensive irrigation system of underground concrete pipe that raised the ultimate cost to nearly four hundred dollars per acre. To some degree, the defects in the property offered an initial advantage for the settlers. The board established a factory to manufacture concrete pipe and hired crews of colonists to install it for the irrigation system. With these wages, settlers supplemented their income until their farms could become productive.[17]

The first unit of land at Delhi opened on May 1, 1920; three additional blocks were offered for sale over the next eighteen months. The property was divided into three categories: 95 farm laborer allotments of 2 acres each; 65 poultry farms, each averaging 0.78 acres; and 234 general farms averaging 30 acres apiece. Whereas dairying had become the major enterprise at Durham, the Delhi settlers were encouraged to pursue poultry and fruit growing. Because orchards required a longer time before they became productive, most settlers found themselves dependent on outside income to survive, much of it from building the irrigation facilities. Fortunately, in 1921 the state loaned an additional million dollars to the colony to continue construction of the irrigation works.[18]

Riding the crest of another apparent success, Mead optimistically told the California Development Association in December 1921 that under his scheme 250,000 colonists would be drawn to the state and some 300 million dollars would be spent on intensive cultivation. Delhi seemed to confirm his observations. The colonists, inspired by the project superintendent, Walter E. Packard, and by the enthusiasm and personal concern Mead showed for their welfare, were developing a camaraderie and cooperation that seemed to counterbalance all obstacles. The settlers repeated the methods of mutual aid that had worked so well at Durham, but extended them beyond economic concord. As the centerpiece of their social life, the colonists erected a community hall with a five-thousand-dollar gift from Edgar M. Wilson and a matching sum that they borrowed. It was dedicated in February 1923 and named

Wilson Hall; an oil portrait of Mead hung in a place of honor in the main room.[19]

By 1923 Elwood Mead was indeed a popular figure and found many journals eager to publish his views. He wrote numerous articles on the two state colonies for the leading publications of the day, including *The New Republic, The American Review of Reviews, Survey, Ladies Home Journal, World's Work,* and *Outlook,* as well as various agricultural, learned, and scientific periodicals. In 1920 he wrote *Helping Men Own Farms,* an explanation of the planned-settlement idea and a description of its operation in Australia and at Durham. The book was favorably reviewed and widely distributed. In addition, magazines and Sunday-newspaper supplements featured the colonies and commented favorably on them in editorial columns. The California professor was acclaimed a "miracle man," and a "practical man with a sound solution to a real problem." Mead welcomed all of this publicity as a chance to spread his ideas, and also as free advertising to attract applicants for the unsold farmlands at Delhi.[20]

Glowing articles about the "contented cultivator" and the "new forty-niners," masked difficulties developing at Delhi. The settlement at Durham had been set up in propitious times, on good soil, and with a careful selection of colonists. By 1922 it seemed to be flourishing. On the other hand, Delhi had been started at the beginning of a prolonged agricultural depression and was on far-less-than-ideal farmland. As a consequence, it became increasingly difficult to attract qualified settlers. The widespread publicity from periodicals brought in thousands of inquiries, as did the assistance of railroad colonization departments, but few of these people had the desired qualifications. The board lowered standards but interest dropped even more, and at the end of 1922 almost 40 percent of the land remained unsold. Meanwhile, persons deemed marginal to succeed, at best, purchased most of what was sold. Optimistic predictions by Mead notwithstanding, the project was foundering. The idle acreage meant that a large part of the repayment to the state's revolving fund could not be met. When the state money ran out, work on the underground irrigation system ceased. Many settlers consequently lost their outside employment and fell behind in their obligations, further aggravating conditions.[21]

Mead watched the affairs at the two colonies closely—in fact, in a manner that often verged on being dictatorial. The Settlement Board had control over loans to the settlers, and Mead discouraged improvements that did not increase income. As head of the board, he wanted assurances that anyone "on the hairline between success and failure" did not overextend himself by borrowing for conveniences under the guise of necessities. Mead did not believe, for example, that the settlers needed or could afford automobiles or the latest agricultural equipment until they paid for their farms. To borrow money, a settler had to submit a detailed budget showing his projected income and outlay. The superintendent sent this information, together with his recommendation, to Mead, who passed on the application.[22]

Discouraging nonessential purchases was certainly admirable, but as conditions at Delhi worsened, Mead seemed to become more generous in extending loans to marginal settlers in order to keep them going. Apparently fearing that too many defaults and the attendant bad publicity from disgruntled or bankrupt farmers would discourage newcomers, Mead and the board allowed more and more of these people to become overextended. Even though these loans were for necessities, the fact was that they were digging themselves into a deeper and deeper economic hole. Meanwhile, the facade of contentment and success was maintained in the midst of constant exhortations to hard work and thrift, and the minute monitoring of settlers' lives. Concern for appearances extended to admonitions against signs of neglect—such as dead trees on one's property—lest it give a bad impression to visitors.[23]

The difficulties at Delhi could not be solved by sacrifice or hidden behind neatly trimmed hedges; the project needed more money. In 1922, two bond issues were proposed to California voters. One called for ten million dollars to provide homes for war veterans, while the other asked three million dollars for land settlement with a veterans' preference clause as a major feature. These latter funds were earmarked for completion of the irrigation system at Delhi and for establishing more colonies in marginal reclamation areas. Mead argued that unless this bond issue was approved, state settlement would cease, some irrigation districts would default, and the investment already made would be lost. Throughout the state, he pointed with pride to his two colonies and to the tremendous amount of free publicity the state had received from stories about them in the nation's press. With the first settlement booming, and the problems of the second not yet apparent, Mead stressed that the plan cost California nothing except the use of its credit.[24]

Opponents of the issue argued that if Durham and Delhi already were a success, then their purpose—as demonstration projects—had been achieved. Hopefully, this would encourage private companies to adopt similar methods, and make continued state paternalism unnecessary. Publicly, Mead defended his policies and encouraged his influential friends to support the measure. Privately, he predicted to other friends that the bond issue would fail, and said that regardless of its outcome he would not accept reappointment as the head of the Land Settlement Board when his term expired early in 1923. At age sixty-four, Mead claimed to be growing weary of the daily demands of directing the operations of the colonies, and longed for the leisure of the classroom. He also wanted to revise *Irrigation Institutions* and devote more time to university duties.[25]

As he had forecast, Californians rejected the issue—but by only 9,000 votes out of 700,000 ballots cast. Although he lamented that he had not worked a little harder, he interpreted such close returns as a vindication of his plan and as proof of the growing interest in land settlement. He claimed that a major factor in the passage of the ten-million-dollar-veterans'-homes bond issue was the success of Durham and Delhi, while the presence of both issues at one election contributed to the defeat of land settlement.[26]

Concurrent with the failure of the land-settlement bond issue, the final section of the Delhi farms opened. Despite Mead's avowed intention to sever his connections with the Land Settlement Board, he could not accept the defeat of his dream for rural rejuvenation. He continued to recruit settlers and to raise money to complete the irrigation system at Delhi. In January 1923, Mead sounded out friends about reintroducing the bond issue, and when he received encouragement his optimism soared. He talked of ten or twenty million dollars, with a provision that it be doled out a million dollars a year. The new governor, Friend W. Richardson, refused to support the idea, however, and nothing came of it. Someone suggested that the California Development Association set up a private land-settlement corporation, but Mead opposed this plan because it would lack "the drawing power of a state agency." Meanwhile, to relieve the immediate financial crisis, the Delhi farmers borrowed 315,000 dollars from the Federal Land Bank. They turned the money over to the Settlement Board, which used it to keep the project operating.[27]

The search continued for settlers to take up the remaining allotments. In January 1923, George Kreutzer made a tour of the East to recruit colonists, but the few who came were more than offset by those who left. Virtually no new land was sold that year. Mead rejected the suggestion of a friend that sales meetings be held throughout the San Joaquin Valley. He did not want "to make too much noise for fear of reaction if the farms were not sold." Instead, he had advertisements placed in the newspapers of the valley, hoping to attract attention to the opportunities at Delhi.[28]

Publicity of a different—potentially disastrous—nature about Delhi surfaced in February. A rumor spread that Japanese families were living at the settlement. The charge was patently absurd. One of the points Mead had stressed in arguing for rural reform in

California was the need to counter the so-called Yellow Peril; if country life could not be made attractive and profitable for white Americans, the Japanese or some other minority would take it over. In fact, the growth of tenant farming in the state alarmed many people, both because it undermined the agrarian ideal and because it tended to be dominated by non-Anglos. One response to this was the laborer allotments. These were established to lessen dependence on migratory help, as well as to prepare people for farming. Despite these facts, even the suggestion that there were Asians at the colony was sufficient to discredit the entire scheme. Mead requested that the superintendent check out the report. Packard asked the American Legion to look into the matter. The Legion, through its post at Delhi, investigated and found that Japanese were living north of the settlement and that a few children of colonists were attending an integrated school in the area. The Legion deplored this arrangement and filed a complaint with the county school trustees, who quickly remedied the situation.[29]

Shortly after the stir over the Japanese was resolved, Mead sailed from San Francisco on a planned six-month trip around the world. George Kreutzer took charge of the two colonies, although Mead remained head of the Land Settlement Board at Governor Richardson's request. About the time Mead left, the situation at Delhi degenerated rapidly. Outside employment had ended when the state funds dried up, over 40 percent of the land lay unsold, and the orchards had not begun to produce (nor would they ever have decent yields, given the poor nature of the soil). Adding to the difficulties was the nationwide agricultural depression. Meanwhile, the cooperation that had marked the spirit of initial success now became an organized effort for relief and protest. With no more expedients to relieve the financial woes, the project languished and Richardson vetoed the idea of investing any more money in the scheme. Most farmers subsisted mainly on the crops they grew and the little money they earned from poultry and dairying, but few were able to meet their repayment schedules to the state.[30]

By the summer of 1923, the Delhi settlement reached a state of desperation. Mead's secretary wrote him in Australia that "if the Islanders [*sic*] have more need for you than we have here they must be in a bad way." Mead returned to the United States at the end of the year. He denounced the settlers as anarchists and told the governor they should pay up or be ousted. Richardson refused to do this, and so Mead severed his connection with the two colonies. In January 1924, the governor appointed C. M. Wooster to head the Land Settlement Board, and at the same time, the state legislature appointed a special committee to investigate conditions at Delhi. Problems continued to mount, with project superintendent Packard now the focus of discontent. One wag poignantly summed up the conditions at Delhi and the feelings of the settlers in a limerick:

> There was a young dictator named Walter
> who came to Delhi to alter.
> He sold some sand and said it was land.
> To the state I am now a defaulter.

Packard resigned in February, shortly after disgruntled farmers, in a fit of frustration, took the oil portrait of Mead and "lynched it" in front of Wilson Hall.[31]

California, meanwhile, took steps to alleviate the distress at Delhi. Based on the special committee's findings, the legislature wrote off the major part of the debt, giving the settlers virtually a fresh start. In the interim, disaffection spread to Durham, where the farmers, now feeling the effects of depressed farm prices as well as soil exhaustion, demanded the same special treatment. The settlers vented their anger against George Kreutzer, whom they had held in high regard until the trouble at Delhi. They pilloried him at various meetings, and ultimately he stood trial on charges of misrepresentation in the sale of one of the farm units. By 1928, officials connected with the two projects saw the hopelessness of continuing the scheme. California officials began litigation to extricate the state from land colonization, and in 1930 an agreement was reached with the settlers. The experiment—or, as Mead insisted on calling it, the demonstration—cost California about two and a half million dollars, not to mention the losses and hardships suffered by the people who had invested their savings in a new plan for helping men own farms.[32]

The settlement scheme was not a total loss. It focused attention on significant problems of rural life in general, and on colonization practices in particular. Private land companies watched the innovations at Durham and Delhi closely. Executives of these firms consulted Mead, and several offered him positions to direct their operations. Railroad colonization departments were especially interested in the Mead plan because each settler represented an estimated gross value to the lines of between 250 dollars to 750 dollars per year. They had backed the original legislation and the bond issues, and had promoted the scheme by distributing thousands of pamphlets to prospective buyers. Moreover, in the sale of their own holdings, the rail lines adopted many of Mead's ideas: initiating liberal terms for purchase and repayment, providing technical advice, and preparing farmsteads for cultivation before sale. Such procedures made it easier to acquire property, but as Durham and Delhi demonstrated, they could not ensure success.[33]

Mead would never acknowledge anything defective in his plan. He insisted that the failures at Durham and Delhi essentially were due to the hostility of Governor Richardson. In 1925, the two men became embroiled in a heated exchange, each blaming the other for the disastrous results of the colonies. Mead contended that Delhi was financially solvent when he resigned, a fact that was technically true even though it was on the verge of collapse. He charged that the governor bitterly opposed land settlement and, when hard times fell on Delhi, had done all he could to wreck it by "intemperate utterances" and by encouraging complaints. The governor claimed that he had not opposed the plan but that when he saw the futility of continuing a losing proposition he had decided to end the state's involvement. Richardson said the fiasco was the result of poor soils, inexperienced settlers, unwise advice, and the "fanciful theories and business incapacities" of Elwood Mead.[34]

The rhetorical broadsides missed several fundamental reasons for the failure. Aside from immediate and obvious difficulties, such as poor land purchased at high prices and bad advice on what to grow on it, there were more basic problems. The prolonged agricultural depression of the 1920s resulted in the bankruptcy of thousands of established farmers. Trying to start a new farm in this period would have been a challenge even to experienced and well-financed pioneers, which few Delhi colonists were. Furthermore, the scheme was tested at a time of rapidly rising urbanization with an inexorable decline in rural life. Additionally, the government's involvement spelled doom for the plan, as the settlers quickly perceived that once involved the state could not afford to abandon them. Finally, Mead was attempting the dichotomy of creating a hearty, independent yeoman by regimented, dictatorial means. In public, he maintained his defense of the scheme and put the blame on Governor Richardson. He confided privately to a friend his real judgement: "Durham should have succeeded; Delhi was a mistake."[35]

SEVEN

━━━━━━━━━

Consulting Around the World

ON APRIL 13, 1933, ELWOOD MEAD, HIS DAUGH-
ter Sue, and son John left San Francisco on the steamship *Maun-
ganui* for Honolulu, the first stop on an around-the-world consulting tour. Officials in Hawaii, Australia, and Palestine had
requested his advice on irrigation and settlement. Since he had not
taken a personal leave from the university in eight years, Mead was
given a six-month leave of absence. He planned to return to the
classroom in January 1924, but upon completion of the tour Secretary of the Interior Hubert Work asked Mead to come to Washington to serve on a special board created to make a thorough
review of reclamation in the United States. When he finished this
task three months later, Mead was offered the position as Commissioner of Reclamation. The trip that started out as a sabbatical
eventually resulted in a permanent separation from the University
of California.[1]

Plans for the trip actually began early in 1922, when officials in
Hawaii and Australia and leaders of the World Zionist Organization requested Mead's advice on settlement problems. Because he
was so heavily involved with his university duties and the two
colonies in California, Mead could arrange only a short trip to
Hawaii at that time. Later in the year, however, the British Am-
bassador to the United States intervened with a request to Uni-

versity of California President David P. Barrows that Mead be
allowed to return to Australia to help the government with additional settlement projects in the Murrumbidgee area of New
South Wales. The Zionists, meanwhile, continued to press Mead
for advice on colonization problems in Palestine. Mead organized
an around-the-world itinerary so he could consult in all three
places, as well as visit irrigation projects along the way. He was
eager to make the journey and looked on the trip as "a little rest
and a change of scene." He believed that after the six-month excursion, he would "bring back a little more vigor, even if I don't
have any more sense."[2]

In January 1923, as the trip took shape, Mead found himself
mentioned as a candidate for secretary of the interior. Albert B.
Fall had been forced out of that position by the Teapot Dome
scandal, and a number of people suggested Mead as his replace-
ment. His most prominent backer, *The New Republic*, lauded Mead
in an editorial, citing his "outstanding ability and zeal for the public welfare." Meanwhile, Mead had written several letters promoting his old Wyoming colleague, Congressman Frank Mondell, for
the position. When Hubert W. Work was named, Mead told a
friend he was flattered to have been considered and was in no way
disappointed at not being selected. He sailed on his voyage ex-
pecting to resume his teaching duties early in 1924.[3]

Mead spent a week in Hawaii, renewing acquaintanceships and
looking over the progress on settlement that had been made since
his visit the year before. In June 1922, he had gone to the islands
at the request of the Hawaiian Homes Commission. This body
was created by Congress in 1921 to direct a program to lease public
lands at nominal rentals to persons of at least one-half Hawaiian
blood. The purpose was to help the Hawaiians regain possession
of their native land. When the bill was drafted, however, the sugar
planters, fearing the loss of the productive public land they were
leasing from the government, managed to get a provision inserted
that excluded sugar lands from the act. As a palliative, the law

provided that 30 percent of the annual receipts from leasing the sugar lands would be used to create a revolving fund to loan Hawaiian natives money for homes, livestock, and improvements on the lands they were to lease. Backers of the legislation stressed its benefits for the preservation of the Hawaiian race. Lost in the rhetoric was the fact that most of the 200,000 acres set aside for the natives was land that no one had ever been able to make productive.[4]

Mead had been shocked by the conditions he saw in 1922. He questioned the basic purpose of government and concluded that in Hawaii it was to "furnish cheap labor for the sugar planters." He likened rural conditions to what he called "nothing but commercial feudalism," and hoped his recommendations would help alleviate some of the natives' misery. He called for a reduction in the size of the plots, which had varied from twenty to one thousand acres, depending upon classification. He knew that the natives would be unable to cultivate plots this size individually and that most of it, therefore, would be contracted to large planters. He proposed that family-size garden plots of one or two acres would be more in keeping with the goal of the legislation; a person could build up his holdings as he improved his skills. Accordingly, the act had been amended early in 1923 to provide for "residence lots" as he had recommended, and these changes were just being implemented when Mead arrived in April.[5]

On his 1922 visit, the California professor naturally had advocated closer settlement as well. He was enthusiastic about an irrigable area on the island of Molokai, which he believed was admirably suited for an initial project, and work on a settlement there began shortly after he returned to California. By the time of Mead's 1923 inspection, some thirteen families had moved into the development. His pleasure at this was muted by disappointment at the slow progress toward creating subsistence homesteads. Contrary to his recommendation, most of the lands were being leased to natives in large plots. Unfortunately, the Molokai colony eventually failed when the spring that furnished fresh water turned salty, and, as Mead predicted, the Hawaiians re-leased their non-irrigable holdings to pineapple growers.[6]

From Hawaii, Mead sailed to Sydney, Australia. He arrived early in May and enrolled his two children in a boarding school so he would have more freedom to travel around the country. When Mead was in Australia from 1907 to 1915, he worked for the state of Victoria. This time he came at the behest of officials in New South Wales. They were planning to resume the development of lands watered by their allotment of the Murray–Murrumbidgee river system. That process had been delayed by World War I. At the end of hostilities, an attempt at soldier settlements in that area proved enormously expensive and unsuccessful. Then, in 1923, the Australian and English governments signed a Migration Agreement providing that three thousand families of the unemployed in Great Britain be relocated in irrigation areas "down under." Before New South Wales leaders invested more money along the Murrumbidgee, however, they decided to have an expert look over the scheme. Mead was paid three hundred pounds per month plus expenses to evaluate and make recommendations about the proposed project.[7]

Dr. Mead was in Australia for nearly four months. He spent a good portion of the time inspecting the areas under consideration and talking with the region's residents. His activities upset several members of the government. For example, while surveying the Murray River, Mead made some favorable comments about areas along the Murrumbidgee. Joseph H. Carruthers, vice president of the Executive Council of New South Wales, construed the remarks as criticism of the government and as a recommendation to concentrate all efforts on the Murrumbidgee. In a rather blunt letter, Carruthers told Mead that the government had adopted a policy for the Murray lands based on a number of factors of which Mead was unaware, that Mead's chief concern was the Murrumbidgee area, and that as a consultant he was embarrassing the state officials.[8]

Had Mead publicized his true thoughts about New South Wales activities in irrigation and settlement, he would have done far worse than embarrass the government. In a private letter to E. F. Benson, a friend in California, he questioned how the state kept "out of the sheriff's hands." The soldier settlement scheme, which had cost New South Wales some twenty-five million dollars, had resulted in about nine thousand veterans taking up land. Two-thirds of these, he estimated, were "incompetents" who would end up as wards of the state because the "whole affair was political" (a conclusion borne out by Mr. Justice Pike in a report to Parliament in 1929). Moreover, Mead claimed that the distribution of water was so badly handled that eighty small towns had to be supplied with the precious liquid by truck, and Sydney itself was menaced by a "water famine." He had gone to Australia specifically to advise on the Murrumbidgee Irrigation Scheme, and he confided to Benson his pessimism about the results. Fearing that most of the settlers would be totally inexperienced, Mead observed that "if they don't try the soul of the man who had charge of them then he can wear a crown in the hereafter without ever thinking about it."[9]

In his recommendations, Mead presented a plan to eliminate or ameliorate the problems he foresaw for the immigrants from England. He made his usual plea for liberal financial terms, careful selection of colonists, farm advisers, and closer settlement. In addition, he proposed a program reminiscent of his plans for Wyoming in the 1890s: irrigated and grazing lands would be linked. Mead believed that the key to development in the Murrumbidgee area was to build up a range industry. He wanted farmers to switch from orchards to lucerne, a variety of alfalfa. Settlers on small farms would grow this crop in cooperation with pastoralists in the neighboring nonirrigated areas. The graziers would be encouraged to introduce sheep that could be fattened on the lucerne farms, or fed the hay in times of drought. In this way, the maximum number of acres would be put to use, and the settlers would be assured an income.[10]

The government incorporated Mead's suggestions into the overall scheme for the Murrumbidgee irrigation area. Unfortunately, the results were disappointing. The farmers resisted planting lucerne because it required more work than pasture grasses. (Those who followed Mead's advice generally found the soil poorly suited to this crop anyway.) Neither could they be persuaded to cooperate with pastoralists. On the other hand, they ignored the Californian's admonitions against enlarged dairy farms, but this proved a blessing as large blocks of land later became a mainstay of the region. Moreover, the projected immigration never materialized, and, of those who came, few had the skills to succeed, as Mead predicted. His proposals to assist the settler helped ameliorate this deficiency, but the cost and bureaucratic bungling neutralized most of these efforts. In short, the Mead mission was not very helpful.[11]

From Australia, Mead and his two children sailed to Singapore, Java, and then Calcutta. From there they took a railroad across India, stopping to look over irrigation works on the Ganges River. At Bombay, the trio boarded a ship for the journey through the Suez Canal to Port Said, and then went to Palestine, where they arrived at Jerusalem early in November.[12]

In all his years of proselytizing closer settlement, Mead found no more receptive audience or better conditions for his ideas than Palestine. Nowhere was a situation so conducive for success; the Zionist dream permeated everything. Settlers wanted to come in such numbers that small farms were a necessity, if for no other reason than to accommodate all of them; Arab hostility made cooperation essential; speculation was impossible because land was provided only to actual colonists; and concerned Jews throughout the world provided generous financial support.[13]

As noted earlier, Mead had been asked to come to Palestine in

1922, but because of other obligations he requested a postpone-
ment for a year. Leaders of the Zionist Organization were anxious
to have his advice and asked Supreme Court Justice Louis Bran-
deis to intervene and persuade Mead to come as soon as possible.
The Zionists planned to open large areas in the Jezreel, Jordan,
and Esdraelon valleys for intensive cultivation and wanted the
California expert to evaluate their plans. Dr. S. E. H. Soskin, who
was to direct the first settlement, pleaded that the fulfillment of
Zionist aspirations depended on the success of the project—which,
in turn, relied on Mead. Although he could not go until 1923,
Mead had all available material relating to irrigation development
in Palestine sent to him so he could familiarize himself with the
situation there.[14]

The idea of recreating a Jewish home state in Palestine had begun in the 1880s. In 1901, the Jewish National Fund was established to acquire land, and by 1914 there were forty-three rural
settlements with some twelve thousand people living on them.
The Balfour Declaration, by which the British government endorsed the idea of Palestine as a national home for the Jews,
spurred new efforts after World War I. By 1922 the number of
agricultural settlements had risen to seventy-three, but the rural
population had gone up by only three thousand persons. Immigrants flocked to the cities, creating a lopsided economic structure
that worried Zionist leaders. They also sought advice on settlement problems peculiar to Palestine. Their most important concerns were the poverty of the immigrants, their low level of agricultural experience, especially in irrigation farming, and the high
degree of idealism that often blinded settlers to practical reality.
They asked Mead to address these issues.[15]

After an extensive tour of the country, Mead submitted his report. In it, he compared Palestine to California. The coastal plain
from Gaza to Haifa, he said, resembled the area from San Diego
to Santa Barbara, and the Valley of the Jordan was like the Impe-

rial Valley. Both places possessed similar possibilities for agricultural development through irrigation. Both places also faced the twin problems of financing and assisting farmers until they could become self-supporting. In Palestine, Zionists should redirect their priorities, he contended, and stop trying "to show how many farms could be created with the smallest amount of money, rather than show what the soil and climate made possible when there was ample money." [16]

Since the Jews in Palestine were already colonizing in groups, Mead suggested ways to improve this process. He felt that each new settlement should have a competent adviser to help compensate for the general lack of agricultural experience. The colonists also needed money, but he warned the Zionists that too "generous financial aid" would tend to make people "wards of the organization." His experience had shown that people needed to invest a stake of 10 to 25 percent in an endeavor to assure their commitment to its success. Palestine was unique, however, in that the Zionist Organization retained title to the land, and the settlers, with few exceptions, had no money to invest. On the other hand, the idea of returning to the homeland of their people was a more compelling motive to do well than any monetary risk. Still, Mead believed, contracts clearly stating the obligations of the colonists and provisions to enforce them rigidly were an absolute necessity. Finally, Mead believed that one self-sustaining colony should be established to serve as a model for the rest. [17]

This ideal settlement would be the first of a limited number of rural communities. Noting that the reclaimable area of Palestine was comparatively small, Mead believed that it should be dominated by a type of agriculture that would embody the finest traditions and aspirations of the Jewish people. The urban–rural imbalance was inevitable, so the limited development in the countryside should reflect a standard of farming excellence that would be a source of pride to the Jewish people. The settlements should give maximum support for an expanding population in the cities, and become tourist attractions in the future. Mead returned to the United States almost rhapsodic over the New Palestine.[18]

Mead's advice and optimism notwithstanding, agriculture in Palestine continued to be plagued by problems. As conditions degenerated, Zionist leaders asked Mead to return and reevaluate the region in 1927. By this time, a number of American Zionists had become concerned that too much money was "wasted on social projects." Agricultural experts, headed by Mead, went to Palestine that summer for a thorough investigation. In December they completed their report, which first addressed an issue basic to success in rural Palestine. Mead and his associates pressed the Zionist leaders to commit themselves to characterizing their role as either philanthropy or business. They emphasized that if philanthropy was the prime end of their rural efforts, the ultimate goal of a self-supporting homeland could never be realized.[19]

The heart of the problem lay in the demands of the socialistic Jewish Federation of Labor (JFL), which had a strong antagonism to capitalism. The JFL pressured the Zionist organizations to fund more and more settlements and to overburden each of them with more people than needed. The extra people sought outside employment, and found it by working for Zionists in establishing more and newer settlements. The net effect gave the appearance of near solvency, when, in fact, Zionist funds were providing a major portion of most settlements' income. The report warned that the JFL must be removed from the agricultural sector and the settlements put on a paying basis. It concluded with a reiteration of Mead's 1924 recommendations for ideal rural communities, ideas crucial to the *kibbutzim* movement which has become so closely identified with modern Israel.[20]

Meanwhile, developments in the United States elevated Mead to the pinnacle of his professional career. When he left Berkeley in April 1923, he had planned to resume teaching the following January. In September, however, Secretary of the Interior Hubert Work wrote to him in Australia and asked that he serve on a Committee of Special Advisers on Reclamation, a body established to study the critical shape that reclamation had reached by 1923. Mead was a natural choice since he had been on the earlier comprehensive investigation of reclamation, the Cost Review Board of 1916. The difficulties identified at that time had been relieved to a great extent by World War I, but as the agricultural depression of the 1920s worsened, irrigated areas once again were suffering. Water users had been granted time extensions for the payment of construction and maintenance charges in 1921, 1922, and 1923, and it was expected that such temporary expedients would be needed the following year. To alleviate these conditions, Work requested that six men apply their "best thought" to finding ways in which reclamation should be "adapted to existing conditions, so that its future success may be achieved and the possibility of home ownership be assured to settlers." Mead agreed to serve on the committee.[21]

The committee, usually referred to as the Fact Finders Committee, began work on October 15, although Mead did not join the group until late December. The investigation covered every aspect of the Reclamation Service, from its inception in 1902. Superintendents of all projects submitted detailed reports, and the files of the Reclamation Service were examined. In Washington, 124 witnesses testified on the various aspects of reclamation, and settlers told their side of the story at a special ten-day meeting in Salt Lake City early in 1924. In addition, Mead made a personal visit to one representative project, the Newlands, Nevada, Irrigation Area, and submitted a written report. From this voluminous collection of material a panorama of the problems of reclamation emerged, and from that composite the Fact Finders made their recommendations.[22]

The Fact Finders submitted a list of sixty-five suggestions that bore the imprint of Mead on every important point. Reviewing the twenty-one-year history of federal activities in reclamation, the committee members found numerous defects and errors, yet they declared the basic program to be sound. Echoing what Mead had been saying for over thirty years, the report called for a shift from engineering considerations to social needs on the projects. Mead always had opposed giving settlers on federal irrigation projects special privileges. He firmly believed that with the proper conditions, reclamation could pay its own way, and he objected to making irrigation farmers "wards" of the state. Palliatives such as debt repudiation, deferred payments, and interest-free construction charges merely whetted the appetite of colonists for more favors. Besides, many people had done extremely well and did not need assistance, while a significant number had lost their farms to banks and mortgage companies who now held the property. The blanket writing-off of debt would give these landowners a better bargain, but it would not provide relief for the deserving settler who needed money to improve his farm or buy better livestock and agricultural implements.[23]

Recognizing that the goal of the Reclamation Act of 1902 had been to create homes, the Fact Finders hoped to propose changes that would allow the original purpose to be achieved. Mead submitted a ten-point plan to the committee that had community settlements as its central feature. He also called for close supervision of farmers, a minimum capital required of applicants, safeguards against land speculation by government retention of titles for ten years, and cooperative efforts by colonists. He further suggested a new system for setting land values and repayment schedules. Based on the crop-producing quality of the soil, an acre would be worth the annual gross income from its cultivation, computed by averaging the returns for the previous ten years. The repayment charge for construction would be 5 percent of the productive power of the land spread over a twenty-year period. Thus if an acre's value was determined to be 120 dollars by this method, it would be amortized at 6 dollars annually until the debt was paid. The committee incorporated these ideas into the report it sent to President Calvin Coolidge. The president transmitted it to Congress and asked that "whatever legislation is necessary to the advancement of reclamation . . . be enacted without delay."[24]

On December 5, 1924, Congress passed the Fact Finders Act, based on the report drawn up by the special advisers. This legislation made significant changes in the operation of federal reclamation. It called for a scientific classification of all project lands and a reassignment of construction costs according to the productive value of those lands. Annual charges were to be based on those land values according to Mead's 5 percent formula. The law further provided for the early transfer of the operation of the irrigation works to water-users associations or irrigation districts. It also declared a moratorium on new construction unless a thorough study showed that a project would be financially solvent and adaptable for settlement. Mead and his associates had recommended aid and direction in land settlement, but instead the measure merely established minimum qualifications for applicants, hoping thereby to improve chances for success.[25]

The passage of this act marked the most important modification in reclamation policy since the federal government entered the field in 1902. Another significant change occurred while the Fact Finders were putting the final touches on their report. David W. Davis, who in 1923 had replaced Arthur Powell Davis as director of the Reclamation Service, resigned. The logical choice to head the Bureau (it had been upgraded to a bureau when D. W. Davis took over) as it moved in a new direction was the man most responsible for formulating the new course. The other five Fact Finders were enthusiastic about the appointment of Elwood Mead, and Secretary Work and the staff of the Bureau felt he was the person best fitted for the job. On March 31, 1924, Mead wrote to President W. W. Campbell to request a year's leave of absence from the University of California so that he could accept the position. Campbell approved the request.[26]

Mead's tour around the world was only moderately successful. He found that the proposals he had made for Hawaii were ac-

cepted only halfheartedly. On the other hand, his recommendations in Australia were well received, but they failed to achieve the
desired result. Palestine was the bright spot of this trip, confirmed
by a return visit in 1927, because it demonstrated as nowhere else
the possibilities of closer settlement. When he got back to the
United States, his own government sought his advice, and here he
made an enduring contribution. He helped put together a program to correct the problems of federal reclamation. In recognition of his contributions in this regard, Mead was then named to
head the Bureau of Reclamation and implement the new policy.

EIGHT

Commissioner of Reclamation

WITH OVER FOUR DECADES OF EXPERIENCE IN
arid problems, Elwood Mead took up his duties as Commissioner
of Reclamation on April 3, 1924. Besides the opportunity to re-
shape reclamation policies, Mead believed that the appointment
would put him in a position to create the planned communities he
had been advocating for the United States since 1915. His first task
was to implement the Fact Finders' recommendations, and by 1929
he had turned federal reclamation around and put it on a more
stable basis. The Great Depression caused a setback in this progress, but Mead's innovations clearly lessened the impact of the economic crisis. He continued in office under the New Deal. During
his final years, he saw a greatly expanded building program for
reclamation, and, at last, the adoption of a national program of
planned communities.[1]

Shortly after taking office, Mead made an extensive tour of the
twenty-four federal projects in operation as well as proposed sites
for new ones. He spent two months in the West examining these
works and talking with settlers. This trip supplemented the knowledge he had acquired as a member of the Fact Finders Committee,
and gave him a comprehensive picture of reclamation conditions.
His conclusions from these studies enforced what he had long advocated: the government should concentrate first on the comple-

tion and full development of the works already begun. New projects, he believed, would spread "too thinly the available funds and talent for accomplishing real success in the whole activity."[2]

Mead's primary concern was—as it had always been—for the actual settler, whom he believed could be successful if given equitable financial arrangements. He resented speculators who profited by the government's improvements but who did nothing themselves to increase the value of their holdings. Likewise, he was displeased with settlers who seemed to hold the Reclamation Bureau responsible for the low price of farm products and the high interest rates of the 1920s. Mead wanted to make it clear that the Bureau was not a "credit agency," nor would it forego its payments so that private financial companies or governmental agencies that had loaned settlers money could be repaid.[3]

In 1924, water users were granted extensions on construction charges for the fourth year in a row, and Mead was determined that this would not happen again. In December, the Fact Finders Act was passed, empowering the commissioner to begin his reordering of reclamation priorities. Implementation of this law, it was assumed, eventually would eliminate the need for deferment of payments. Meanwhile, the commissioner and the secretary of the interior announced that there would be no more blanket moratoriums. Further alterations in money due the government would be decided on an individual basis. By this ruling, Mead hoped not only to collect the amounts owed, but also to force persons holding idle yet irrigable land to put it to use. Neither land speculators nor solvent farmers would be granted blanket concessions, he announced, because it would have a "demoralizing influence" to reward the unworthy so the deserving may be benefited.[4]

Mead insisted that the payment of money due the government was essential to the integrity of the reclamation program. In the five years from 1920 through 1924, the sum of 8,652,610 dollars—construction charges of 5,222,331 dollars and operation and maintenance charges of 3,430,279 dollars—went uncollected. Over 3 million dollars of this amount resulted from the 1924 moratorium. Mead blamed the progressive increase in deficiences on the ease with which deferments were obtained and on the laxity that many worthy, struggling settlers came to feel about their government obligations when they saw people who could afford to pay neglecting these debts with impunity.[5]

When it became clear that Mead intended to enforce his new regulations, most people responded and there was a steady improvement in collections. The fiscal year 1926 showed an increase of 641,251 dollars in payments, and this upward trend continued until the depression. Total payments in 1925 were 3,811,620 dollars, while in 1929 they amounted to 6,308,314 dollars.[6]

In the long run, this "get tough" policy was successful. At first, however, there was considerable opposition to it, especially on those projects with the poorest repayment records. For example, at North Platte, Nebraska, Mead's threat to cut off water unless payments were forthcoming resulted in the hanging in effigy of the commissioner and the secretary of the interior. True to life, the "dummy" representing Mead had only one arm.[7]

At Belle Fourche, South Dakota, where only about 15 percent of the money due the government between 1920 and 1924 had been paid, the water users were in arrears over one million dollars. Resident owners occupied only 31 percent of the land; the rest was either leased out or abandoned. Even after Mead made clear that his main concern was the collection of charges for operation and maintenance, the settlers balked. They questioned why the government should not show the same indulgence toward its citizens that it was showing toward foreign countries over war debts. They also pointed to the 5 percent formula for contracts provided in the Fact Finders Act. Although Belle Fourche water users had not entered such an agreement with the government, they noted that they had paid 472,000 dollars for construction in the preceding sixteen years, an average of 30,000 dollars annually. The gross crop returns from 1921 to 1924 averaged 560,000 dollars per year, 5 percent of which was 28,000 dollars. If Mead's formula for repayment of construction costs was applied to their project, they actually had overpaid![8]

The 5 percent formula, designed to provide an equitable plan for repayment, was based on the productive value of the soil. A defect in the legislation fixed no period in which the total construction obligation was to be repaid. The Bureau entered into new contracts with water users on nine projects, including Sun River, Montana, whose repayment could take a century, and North Platte, Nebraska, where estimates ran up to ninety years. Congress repealed this aspect of the law in the Omnibus Adjustment Act of 1926, and set a maximum amortization period of forty years, but contracts entered into under the 1924 Act remained in force. Mead's brief effort in tying repayment to production proved that there was no correlation between the cost of construction and its value to reclaimed lands.[9]

The Omnibus Act of 1926, which repealed the 5 percent plan, also contained provisions for adjusting construction charges. Mead felt that it would make collections easier if water users did not feel that they were paying for the government's mistakes. Expectations of significant write-offs, in fact, had contributed to the problem of collection since 1924, when the Fact Finders had called for a scientific study, classification, and valuation of all projects lands. They had recommended that construction repayments be written off on those lands that did not "possess a productive power sufficient to support the farmer's family" as well as areas "just coming into agricultural production and not yet ready to begin repayments." A Board of Survey and Adjustment was created to fix the amounts to be charged off. Based on the board's findings, Congress approved government assumption of losses amounting to 14,667,965 dollars on land "permanently nonagricultural under the practices of irrigation farming." It also suspended construction payments of 12,788,406 dollars on land deemed un-productive without expensive improvements.[10]

In addition to construction charges, irrigation farmers were as-sessed an annual operation and maintenance fee. The Fact Finders had recommended that the supervision of the day-to-day manage-ment of facilities be turned over to the people on the land, noting that the Reclamation Act of 1902 had called for such an arrange-ment when the major portion of construction costs were repaid. This would make water users responsible for the collection of operating and maintenance charges, and thus they would share responsibility for the work of reclamation. Consequently, they would be more aware of the expenses involved. When Mead took office, only the Salt River, Arizona, and a division of the Mini-doka, Idaho, projects had assumed such duties. In 1926, Mead began a policy of decentralization by transferring these functions to local control. Interior Secretary Work, President Coolidge, and Congress all encouraged his actions. Within a year, a dozen water-user associations entered these agreements, and ultimately all of the projects adopted the plan. The result was a boost in morale and an improvement in collections, as farmers became involved in running and repairing their own irrigation systems.[11]

These actions were remedial, designed to correct past errors and to return reclamation to its original purpose. To the chagrin of Western irrigationists, Mead insisted that no additional works be built until those in existence were fully developed and settled—or until the need for new ones was clearly demonstrated and shown to be financially sound. The Fact Finders Act had barred further projects until expert information was available as to water supply, land prices, costs, engineering features, adaptability for settle-ment, and feasibility. In 1924, Congress had authorized two new projects and major additions to four others in spite of Mead's ad-monitions and before the Fact Finders law was passed. Mead de-layed and then gradually authorized construction of each of these as studies were done. When a comprehensive survey was finished in 1926, the Commissioner announced a ten-year plan for the completion of all operating facilities. He estimated that annual expenditures of eight to ten million dollars would enable this "conservative program" to be fulfilled.[12]

Yet another issue addressed in the 1926 Omnibus Adjustment Act was the 160-acre limitation. As the professed goal of the Newlands Act had been the creation of family farms, no one was to get more water than what was needed for a quarter section—the basic Homestead unit. Unfortunately, loopholes, and in many cases outright fraud, rendered this provision meaningless and made a mockery of the spirit—if not the letter—of the 1902 Law. For example, a family of four could claim a 640-acre allotment, and file for even more using extended family members and in-laws. Monitoring, challenging or denying such claims was virtually impossible. Mead had a clause inserted in the Omnibus Act requiring water users to sell within a reasonable time at reasonable prices any excess land holdings. Well intended as this might have been, and determined though the Commissioner seemed, little came of these efforts. Mead railed against these abuses in speeches and in the *New Reclamation Era,* but such admonitions were as far as he went. Given the nature of the problem, and the determination of entrenched interests, it was about as much as he was able to do.[13]

Two additional concerns frustrated Mead. They were securing settlers and land speculation. The Fact Finders had called for greater involvement in federal reclamation by state and local entities. Mead believed that a mutual effort to colonize government lands would offer an ideal area of cooperation. As far as people making excessive profits on property in private hands, Mead decided that the best way to discourage speculation was to have the Bureau appraise and set prices on land. If the land sold above the value put on it by the Bureau, one-half of the excess would be applied to construction charges.[14]

Mead's initial attempt to try these ideas illustrated the difficulties involved. The commissioner tested his new policies on the nine-million-dollar Kittitas extension to the Yakima, Washington, project, which was begun in 1925. Mead had inserted into the contract a requirement that committed the state to assist with settlement. Washington's governor, Roland P. Hartley, agreed in principle, but he balked at spending money to fulfill the state's obligation. After considerable wrangling, the state legislature passed what proved to be a wholly unworkable law, but by then construction had begun. There was no way to force compliance, although Mead pressured Yakima organizations concerned with the project's success to give some assistance.[15]

The valuation of land likewise caused controversy. The contract provided that if private land sold above the appraised price, one-half of the excess would be applied to construction costs. After appraisal prices were announced, many landowners complained that the low values prevented them from obtaining loans to complete the necessary irrigation facilities, while others threatened to retain their property and lease it. Believing that tenantry was the worst of evils, Mead was forced to allow upward valuation. He warned that he might discontinue construction, but Washingtonians perceived this to be the empty threat it turned out to be. On subsequent projects, the Bureau continued to seek state cooperation and to check speculation, but with only mediocre results. These factors diminished in importance, however, as the Bureau moved in the 1930s to the multipurpose, entire river-basin development, especially where hydroelectric production was possible.[16]

As his first year in office drew to a close, Mead noted that, although "the spirit of the times is rather reactionary," the progress that had been made was remarkable. Indeed, by implementing the Fact Finders Act, he had brought about a significant transformation in federal reclamation. The commissioner attributed his success in large part to the "confidence in me on the Hill"; Congress was receptive to his ideas. Yet nothing had been done about the one innovation that he most desired—aided and directed settlement. Mead now turned his attention to this issue.[17]

Early in 1925, Mead helped to draft the Kendrick–Winter bill, legislation that would provide a variety of new services on all future projects. These included the increased dissemination of agricultural knowledge among water users; the hiring of advisers to assist settlers on economic and farm matters and to help in organizing cooperatives; and the establishment of a fund to provide long-term, low-interest loans for equipment and permanent improvements. Although the bill was never brought to a vote, Mead was not disappointed. He viewed the introduction of the measure and the publicity it received as an important step in educating people to the need for this type of governmental reclamation activity.[18]

The next year a more modest measure, providing 500,000 dollars to finance two demonstration colonies with one hundred settlers for each, was appended to the Interior Department's annual appropriation. The Senate, however, deleted the item. Mead blamed rejection of the proposal partly on the adverse publicity resulting from California Governor Richardson's attacks on Durham and Delhi, and partly because opponents branded it as socialistic. The commissioner defended his ideas, noting that "anyone who advocates something different from the past is almost certain to be misunderstood." To charges that he was "socialistic and impractical," he refused to "attempt to establish an alibi" for the latter, but emphatically denied the former. In 1928, Mead tried again to secure funds. This time, a 500,000 dollar request was to be restricted to loans for permanent improvements. When the Bureau of the Budget disallowed the request, Mead wrote President Coolidge that "the conservative aid . . . in the bill . . . ought to be given a trial." If the money was not spent to help salvage existing projects, he claimed, it would be spent on building canals for new ones. However, the legislation conflicted with the president's financial program, and he refused to reconsider the proposal.[19]

While he pushed the idea of community settlements in the West, Mead also pursued the possibilities of extending them into the South. After his return from Australia, he had become interested in the reclamation of swampy and cutover lands outside of the arid regions. Through his work for soldier settlements, Mead met Hugh McRae, a wealthy North Carolinian, and because of their mutual interests they became friends. Around the turn of the century, McRae decided to use part of his fortune to set up planned farm colonies to show southerners the benefits of diversified agriculture. By 1908 he had launched six such communities in North Carolina, with moderate success. In the early 1920s, Mead, McRae, and several others tried to induce private capital to invest in a model development that would include the advantages of town and country. When they failed to obtain financial backing for this scheme, McRae and Mead, who had become Commissioner of Reclamation, turned to the federal government to finance a settlement plan for the South.[20]

In 1924, Congress added fifteen thousand dollars to the Reclamation Bureau appropriation for an investigation of the possibilities of developing cutover land and swampland. Mead headed a three-member advisory committee that examined opportunities in the South. The panel recommended the creation of demonstration farm colonies similar to Durham and Delhi in all of the southeastern states. Their findings led to a conference in Washington, in December 1927, to discuss "the promotion of better rural conditions and a more advanced type of agriculture in the South." In his invitation to delegates, Mead indicated his concern for the plight of blacks and unskilled white farmers, who "as tenants or hired laborers are unsuited to any but the most primitive farm practices." Representatives from seven southern states and other interested persons from around the country met with officials of the Interior Department and the Bureau of Reclamation to for-mulate a plan to secure federal funds for establishing planned communities to replace the dreary conditions of Southern rural life.[21]

The following year legislation was introduced in Congress for ten million dollars to set up demonstration colonies in eleven southern states. Interior Secretary Work had warned Mead, after the Washington conference, that he doubted Congress would "be interested in our embarking on reclamation in the South in view of [the] experience with it in the West." Lawmakers never brought the bill to a vote, but they renewed the fifteen-thousand-dollar grant for continued study of the issue. In 1929, Commissioner Mead tried again, but the new secretary of the interior, Ray Lyman Wilbur, rejected the idea, advising Mead candidly that such a project was "one of agriculture and settlement and not of reclamation." Mead persisted, but without administration backing—and because of vigorous opposition from the Agriculture Department—there was little hope of any action. In 1932, after he again unsuccessfully solicited Wilbur on a settlement bill for the South, Mead concluded that "the present financial situation" mitigated against passage of a measure that was "not absolutely essential just now."[22]

The setbacks over his planned-settlement schemes did not diminish Mead's accomplishments during his first five years as Commissioner of Reclamation. Under his direction, the federal government made great advances toward correcting flaws that had plagued the reclamation program since its inception a quarter-century earlier. Problems continued—over 500,000 dollars was deferred in 1929 on payments due from water users—but the general trend steadily improved until the depression of the 1930s. Mead justifiably took pride in the transformation he was bringing about. In 1928, as Mead's seventieth birthday drew near, Secretary Work had requested that the Civil Service Commission allow him to continue for two more years because of his "inestimable value" to the Bureau. Mead originally had planned to stay in Washington for only one year, but each time he faced the prospect of retiring, he decided to extend his commitment.[23]

Mead could not bring himself to quit. He liked Washington and loved his work. Reluctant at first to sever his ties with California, he soon became comfortable in the nation's capital. His yearly salary of ten thousand dollars allowed him to live well, while the social life offered a frequent and welcome respite from arduous office duties. The Meads were seldom at a loss for something to do. They went to receptions at the White House and to dinners or parties at the homes of prominent politicians and government officials. Mead also enjoyed the camaraderie of the Cosmos Club, where he spent many evenings. When not attending some function, Mead followed a regular routine. Each working day, he would come home early and take a bath and nap before dinner. He rose about four in the morning and worked while everything was quiet—a habit he formed as a student at Purdue. His favorite relaxation was playing "500"; he passed many evenings at home beating guests at this card game.[24]

Mead spent considerable time away from Washington. He made at least one trip each spring to the West to inspect reclamation projects. As commissioner, he was also invited to speak before numerous groups and to consult on water problems in various places. In 1926, he went to Cuba to advise officials on hydraulic development and to Haiti to examine irrigation possibilities there. The following year he was absent from the office from April until the middle of June, attending a Pan-Pacific Conference in Honolulu, and from August to October he was in Palestine for the Zionist Organization of America. In 1929, he and Mrs. Mead journeyed to Mexico City, where the commissioner served as chief of the team negotiating an agreement with Mexico over the waters of the Colorado and Rio Grande rivers. These international travels ended after 1929 because of his preoccupation with Bureau business—especially the Colorado River project and depression-related problems. As he grew older, the trips abroad also became too strenuous. In the 1930s, Mead limited himself to western tours and his duties in Washington.[25]

The Meads lived in an apartment in Washington until 1928, when they purchased a comfortable house at 1661 Crescent Place. The family became smaller each year. Tom and his wife lived in the West, Lucy had married Morrill Marston, and Sue was away at school. John attended West Point, which pleased his father immensely. Katherine, the daughter who had been retarded from birth, died in 1928. Only a grown son, Arthur, who suffered from mental illness, remained at home. He caused his father untold worry and problems by his frequent disappearances. Mead relied on Katherine's nurse, Hilda Blaylock, and his friend George Kreutzer to find Arthur and bring him back. (Kreutzer had become chief of Reclamation Economics in 1925, after he resigned from the superintendency of Durham.) When the situation became unmanageable in 1928, Mead asked Kreutzer to commit Arthur to a mental institution; he did not have the heart to do so himself. The Meads went to see their son often and brought him home to visit whenever they could. It was an added grief for the commissioner when George Kreutzer died suddenly of a heart attack in November 1929.[26]

The depression, which started in 1929, disrupted the steady improvement in reclamation that had begun with the Fact Finders' inquiry. The total value of irrigated crops had risen from 65,046,300 dollars in 1923 to 161,179,880 dollars in 1929. This was accomplished despite the generally depressed state of agriculture during the decade. However, by 1931 the value of irrigated farm goods had fallen to 73,960,377 dollars. Because of this precipitate drop, water users failed to meet their payments to the government and began petitioning for a five-year moratorium on construction costs. Mead incurred the enmity of people on the projects when he opposed a blanket deferment, and urged, instead, yearly suspensions to individuals on the basis of need. As the situation worsened, he relented in April 1932, and Congress passed a bill that deferred construction payments for 1931. Without such action, the Bureau could not have provided water legally for a majority of the irrigators. The law forbade delivery to anyone who was twelve months in arrears on construction payments. Eventually, Congress granted deferments for five years—until 1936—and extended the repayment period to make up for the lapse.[27]

Many irrigators also demanded suspension of operation and maintenance charges. Mead marshalled figures to show that in spite of water users' claims, this action was unnecessary and would "demoralize reclamation finances." At the Orland project in California, for example, 98 percent of the cultivated farms had paid operating charges in 1933. The commissioner was adamantly opposed to favoritism toward people living on lands watered by the government. In a November letter to the new secretary of the interior, Harold L. Ickes, Mead argued that people on private irrigation projects received no special treatment and that if federal reclamation was to continue it ought to be kept a "business institution." He pointed out that movements for relief were often the work of "demagogues who trump up reasons why these debts should not be paid." He warned Ickes against uncritical acceptance of water users' petitions, noting that the Bureau's policy of insistence had resulted in the collection of most operating funds due the government. Despite this policy, receipts declined, but, in general, Mead trimmed expenses to make up for much of the deficit.[28]

The suspension of construction payments in 1931 created serious difficulties because the building of new projects, as well as the completion of old ones, depended on these funds. Even before the moratoriums, receipts had fallen and revenues from land sales and royalties from oil leases, both earmarked for reclamation construction, dropped one-third below former amounts. This meant hardships for the farmers, who needed additional facilities, and for construction workers, who relied on the building program for a livelihood. In 1926, Mead had convinced Congress to appropriate funds from the Treasury directly to reclamation for the first time. An allotment of 2.3 million dollars was used to tide the Bureau over until the Fact Finders' recommendations took effect.[29]

Five years later, Mead returned for an advance of 5 million dollars to the Bureau for its construction program. These funds, with other accretions, gave reclamation officials over 7¼ million dollars to spend during the fiscal year 1932. Lawmakers provided no such funds the next year, however, and the Bureau spent less than 3½ million dollars for construction. During that same twelve-month period, the total value of irrigated crops slipped to 50,158,381 dollars.[30]

Despite these gloomy statistics, the basic structure of the federal reclamation program was sound when Franklin D. Roosevelt took office in March 1933. The fundamental problem was that irrigation farmers, like farmers everywhere, were in distress because of low prices: government action to raise agricultural prices was the ultimate solution. In terms of the Reclamation Bureau under Mead, the deepening economic depression caused delayed repayments on construction charges, but it did not result in defaults. Meanwhile, the ledger of operating and maintenance expenses was kept within a reasonable imbalance. Some water users, piqued because he did not accede to their wishes, opposed Mead's reappointment, but a majority applauded when President Roosevelt retained the seventy-five-year-old commissioner in office.[31]

That Mead survived the transition from Hoover to the New Deal was more than a tribute to his reputation as something of an icon of irrigation. He was an articulate spokesman for his beliefs and understood the necessity and value of a positive image. Early in his tenure, he took the offensive in presenting the Reclamation Bureau's story through a highly successful public relations operation. Recognizing that farm surpluses, and the attendant low prices of the 1920s, threatened his agency, he gathered facts and figures to show that the products of irrigation were not in com-

petition with crops grown by conventional means. Moreov
stressed reclamation benefits to the West—in such terms as ..-
chasing power of project residents, crop revenues and hydroelectric power produced—to garner support from Congress and
the public. In fact, the Bureau flourished under the New Deal.[32]

Mead managed the Reclamation Bureau for Roosevelt much as
he had under Coolidge and Hoover. From the beginning, however, he and Interior Secretary Ickes clashed. They conflicted initially over Ickes's attempt to swap certain department functions,
including reclamation, with Agriculture Secretary Henry A. Wallace. That trade fell through when Wallace changed his mind, but
it set the tone for relations between Mead and his boss. More
friction came when Ickes, fearing another Teapot Dome scandal,
carried his suspicion of people as far as wastebasket searches. This
practice upset Mead, who threatened at one point to resign and
go public with this information unless the searches ceased. Thereafter, a coolness prevailed for the remainder of Mead's tenure. But,
as Mead told Ray Lyman Wilbur, the prior secretary, "the part of
his [Ickes's] team that knows its onions is left alone." This tolera-
tion became more pronounced as Ickes came to appreciate the importance of hydroelectric power.[33]

The Reclamation Bureau's involvement with hydroelectric
power came more by accident than design. The Salt River facility
in Arizona was the first major project to generate electricity to
make the concrete needed for its construction. Thereafter the excess power on this—and a growing number of projects—was used
to operate pumping machinery. Soon the excess was being sold
and the proceeds used to meet a portion of water user obligations.
By the 1920s, power revenues increasingly constituted a significant
factor in the economics of reclamation undertakings. When Mead
took charge of the Bureau, he began to channel his agency toward
a whole river basin concept in which hydroelectric power assumed
a central role. This process reached its high point with the Boulder

Canyon Act. Dependence on hydroelectric power income as a part of watershed-wide development had arrived and became an integral aspect of Bureau operations.[34]

Under the New Deal, the Bureau's construction program was vastly enlarged. Mead was a careful spender, yet because of the Bureau's long-range planning and feasibility studies, he was able to begin building as soon as funds were available. By the middle of 1934, the Public Works Administration (PWA) had allotted 103,535,000 dollars for existing or new reclamation projects. While the PWA basically took over its construction activities, Bureau engineers continued to supervise and draw up plans. In addition, they did the design and specification work for the Tennessee Valley Authority project.[35]

When the work force was enlarged to handle the increased activity after 1933, PWA funds paid the new employees, who did not have civil service status under that program. Instead, they had to get clearance from the Democratic party organization in the locale from which they came. Mead felt that this was "theoretically . . . all wrong," but "practically, we have had but little difficulty," since unsatisfactory men were not forced on the bureau. Local Democratic party authorities tended to clear everyone from their area, regardless of political affiliation.[36]

Mead had built up an efficient staff over the years, and in general, they were both competent and loyal. His secretary, Mae A. Schnurr, for example, was a devoted assistant who served as acting commissioner during some of his lengthy absences from Washington. As such, she is believed to be the first woman in the history of the federal government to head a major bureau. George Kreutzer was another invaluable aide. On the other hand, Porter W. Dent, the assistant commissioner and a twenty-year veteran of the bureau, was forced to resign in 1934. Apparently, he aspired to Mead's job and was discovered sending people on projects letters telling them what he would do for them if he were in charge. After his dismissal, Dent sent a scathing fifty-five-page indictment of the commissioner to Ickes (who had no love for Mead), but the secretary dismissed the complaint as having "no foundation." John C. Page, chief administrative assistant of construction at Hoover Dam, was then transferred to Washington and groomed as Mead's successor.[37]

Mead's primary concern was running the Reclamation Bureau, but he also took an active interest in the Subsistence Homesteads Program of the New Deal. Since his return from Australia, Mead had continually pushed the idea of government-planned communities. His efforts to establish soldier settlements after World War I failed, and Durham and Delhi had not worked out. When he became commissioner, Mead tried to secure funds to organize colonies in the West and later in the South, but he was unable to obtain sufficient congressional support. Finally, Senator John H. Bankhead of Alabama included an appropriation for subsistence homesteads in the National Industrial Relief Act of 1933. After Mead had proselytized and publicized the idea for two decades, the federal government adopted a national scheme for model communities.[38]

Mead was not officially connected with the Subsistence Homesteads Division of the Interior Department or the Resettlement Administration, which absorbed it in 1935, but his influence was unmistakable. He helped to develop the specifications that transformed the general provisions of the law into reality in 1933, and was mentioned as a possible head of the new agency. However, the job went to a younger man, Milburn Lincoln Wilson, who acknowledged that most of his basic ideas on subsistence homesteads came from Mead. Although the commissioner was not involved in subsequent decisions, he watched the program closely. Mead had always tied his plans for rural communities to reclamation, but the directors of the Subsistence Homesteads Division rejected this idea. In 1934, when he suggested the Belle Fourche, South Dakota, reclamation project for subsistence development, they turned down the plan because they did not want to create a

unit completely financed by the government. Still, the basic concept of planned rural communities owed more to Mead than to
any other man; the New Deal program for subsistence homes was
the fruition of the one idea he cherished most.[39]

In his twelve years as Commissioner of Reclamation, Elwood
Mead managed to accomplish virtually everything he had set out
to do. He took over a bankrupt bureau in 1924 and transformed it
into an agency that was not only able to survive the early years of
the depression without massive public funds, but also to thrive
under the New Deal. His genius both as a policymaker and as an
administrator enabled him to find solutions for reclamation problems and to carry out the needed reforms. In January 1929, when
he was seventy-one years old, there was speculation that Mead
would retire. He had already completed the restructuring of the
Reclamation Bureau—a triumph for any man—yet he could not
give up the work he loved so much. Plans for the development of
the Colorado River were then moving to the construction stage.
The gigantic dam planned for Boulder Canyon, he wrote his son
Tom, would doubtless give him increased "prestige," and he
wanted to "stay on for two more years if my health holds good."
In the end, Mead lived to see this project through to completion.[40]

NINE

Building Boulder Dam

THE BUILDING OF BOULDER DAM WAS ONE OF the outstanding engineering feats of the twentieth century, an accomplishment on a scale with the Panama Canal. Elwood Mead was involved in this project almost from its inception and, as Commissioner of Reclamation, oversaw the construction of what was the most expensive and largest single reclamation project the United States had ever undertaken. With no precedent for such a mammoth task, Mead was responsible for the gigantic operation, moving both men and material to a remote, barren section of the country to erect this huge structure. The dam was finished in 1936, a full two years ahead of schedule.[1]

The Colorado River watershed, which covers parts of seven states in the United States and a small portion of the Republic of Mexico, is roughly divided into two basins. The upper basin consists of the drainage area in Wyoming, Utah, Colorado, and New Mexico, while the lower basin includes parts of Arizona, California, Nevada, and Mexico. The two areas are separated by the "canyon region"—a three-hundred-mile "geologic bottleneck" in southern Utah and northern Arizona. In the lower basin are broad alluvial plateaus in its northern reaches and a rich delta region to the south, which includes the fertile Imperial Valley.

Development of the Imperial Valley in California began around

Colorado River Basin

WYOMING

Green River

Great
Salt
Lake

U p p e r
B a s i n

0   75   150
Miles

UTAH

Colorado River

NEVADA

COLORADO

Lake
Powell

Virgin River

Paria R.

San Juan River

Lee Ferry

Lake
Mead

Hoover
Dam

ARIZONA

Little Colorado River

Santa Fe

CALIFORNIA

L o w e r
B a s i n

Los Angeles

Colorado
River
Aqueduct

Colorado River

Bill Williams R.

Parker Dam

Salt R.

NEW MEXICO

Rio Grande

San
Diego

All-
American
Canal

Imperial
Dam

Gila River

Yuma

Alamo
Canal

Baja California

Gulf of
California

MEXICO

El Paso

the turn of the century, and by 1903 some two thousand settlers were farming there. They obtained water for irrigation from the Colorado by a canal that began at the United States–Mexico boundary and ran west through 137 miles of Mexican territory. The river, however, was undependable, alternating between scarcity and flood. Because 1903 and 1904 were dry years, additional cuts were made in the riverbank to allow more water to flow into the canal. When, in 1905, the Colorado discharged an unusually heavy volume of water, the closures of the cuts failed. The swollen river flooded the valley, caused millions of dollars worth of damage, and filled the Salton Sea. After two years of struggle, the levees were rebuilt and the river returned to its channels. This disaster, costly though it was, served to focus the attention of the nation on the problems of the Colorado.[2]

When floods were not a menace, droughts threatened the existence of the farmers in this region. Some years they had to haul water for domestic use and for livestock as far as one hundred miles. The residents of the valley were uneasy, furthermore, because their water supply depended on conditions in Mexico. The canal ran through the northern section of Baja California, and a 1904 agreement with Mexico gave that country the right to one-half of the water supply on demand, a stipulation that retarded expansion in the Imperial Valley. Political instability south of the border added to their anxiety, as did the threat of floods from the poorly maintained canal. In short, their concerns alternated between whether they would get enough or too much water. Despite these difficulties, the area under cultivation in the Imperial Valley increased rapidly, and by 1910 there were 180,000 acres in crops. Then, in 1918, farmers formed the Coachella Valley County Water District in the area north of the Imperial Valley. At the time, district directors announced that only about 10,000 acres of the 250,000 irrigable acres in the Coachella Valley could be adequately supplied by underground water. The need for water to put this land to use, added to the desire to free the Imperial Valley from reliance on Mexico, caused agitation for the construction of a canal located entirely in the United States.[3]

In 1916, Mead and two engineers, D. C. Henny and Joseph Jacobs, had investigated the problems of irrigation and flood control in the Imperial Valley. In their report, drawn up in March 1917, they emphasized that the "political obstacles" caused by the location of a large portion of the works in Mexico were as serious as the physical difficulties in operating the enterprise. The Mexican government forbade the corporation that controlled the canal from entering into arrangements with a foreign government. This provision, the report noted, barred action on flood control in Mexico by the Reclamation Service. Furthermore, Mead confided to Benjamin Wheeler at Berkeley, the governor of Baja California was an "irresponsible dictator" who constantly harassed the Mexican canal company for bribes. The three men recommended that further investigations explore ways to free the Imperial and Coachella valleys from these problems.[4]

The following year, Congress established an All-American Canal Board, consisting of Mead, Carl E. Grunsky of the Imperial Irrigation District, and W. W. Schlecht of the Reclamation Service. The three men were to supervise surveys and make recommendations on a canal located entirely in the United States. Their report, submitted to Interior Secretary Franklin K. Lane in July 1919, advocated a new canal situated entirely in California, and estimated it would cost over fifteen million dollars. However, Arthur Powell Davis, director of the Reclamation Service, opposed the plan because it dealt strictly with a canal. Davis had been an advocate of the comprehensive development of the Colorado since the turn of the century. He feared that independent construction of the canal would frustrate plans to solve fundamental issues such as silting and floods—or a water-rights agreement with Mexico. He was sufficiently persuasive, and Congress appropriated funds for further study of all phases of the Colorado River question.[5]

The new study was submitted to Interior Secretary Albert B. Fall by Reclamation Director Davis in February 1922. Generally known as the Fall–Davis report, it surveyed the problems of the lower Colorado region and called for the construction of an All-American Canal, with costs reimbursed by the water users. Reflecting Mead's influence, the document recommended that public lands reclaimed by these works be reserved for ex-servicemen "under conditions securing actual settlement and cultivation." Concomitant with construction of the canal was to be the building of a multipurpose dam at or near Boulder Canyon, "to be reimbursed by the revenues from leasing the power privileges incident thereto." Finally, the report established priorities for the development: the first consideration would be river regulation and flood control, followed by water storage for irrigation, and then hydroelectric-power production.[6]

While technical studies were being conducted, efforts went forward to settle the interstate and international complications inherent to the development of the Colorado. Each of the seven states in the watershed wanted a guarantee that it would receive an equitable share of the water. After prolonged negotiations, the Colorado River Compact was signed in November 1922 at Santa Fe, New Mexico. Although based on a conservative estimate of 15 million acre-feet, the pact assumed an annual flow of 18 million acre-feet. The agreement gave 7½ million acre-feet to each basin and left the specific allotments to be decided by the states in each basin. The lower basin was allowed 1 million acre-feet of the surplus, while the remaining 2 million acre-feet were not apportioned. Herbert Hoover, the federal representative at these meetings, sponsored a provision that any water given to Mexico should come from the surplus or be shared equally by each basin in the event of a deficiency. The stipulation was accepted, although Mexican objections or claims appear to have been of little concern to Americans interested in improving the Colorado River.[7]

With the Colorado River Basin states' general acceptance of the compact (Arizona refused), sponsors of the project proceeded with engineering studies and efforts to obtain the federal financing to build the huge works. In Washington the fight was led by California Representative Phil D. Swing, who had been chief counsel for the Imperial Irrigation District prior to his election to the House in 1920, and by the influential Senator Hiram V. Johnson, also from California. In the spring of 1922 they introduced the Swing–Johnson bill, which embodied the recommendations of the Fall–Davis report. Their measure did not pass—nor did those they sponsored in 1924 and 1926.[8]

When Mead took office as Commissioner of Reclamation in 1924, he became directly involved in the Boulder Canyon project. His bureau would implement the plan if Congress authorized construction. Mead worked closely with Swing and Johnson to secure legislative passage. He tried to persuade Johnson to include provisions for aid and direction in settlement on the lands opened by the project. Although the senator claimed to see the need for such a stipulation, he demurred, reluctant to add another issue to the fight for passage. Meanwhile, the increasing needs of Los Angeles for domestic water, the continued danger to the Imperial Valley, and a lessening opposition by private-power interests aided the cause. The power companies were mollified by a provision in the law that left open the decision whether the power plant would be in the hands of government or private companies. Congress approved the Swing–Johnson measure, and on December 21, 1928, President Calvin Coolidge signed the bill, known as the Boulder Canyon Project Act.[9]

The Boulder Canyon Project Act established the Colorado River Dam Fund, and authorized the Treasury Department to advance up to 165 million dollars to the Bureau of Reclamation to finance it. The project included a dam with a reservoir of at least twenty-six million acre-feet capacity at Black Canyon or Boulder Canyon, and the All-American Canal to the Imperial and Coachella valleys. The bill estimated the cost of the dam and power plant at approximately 110 million dollars, while the canal was figured at 38,500,000 dollars. The remainder of the sum was for interest during construction. The canal would be repaid by the water users. Of the total amount expended for the dam and power plant, 25 million dollars was allotted for flood control and would be repaid out of surpluses, while 17,717,000 dollars for power-plant machinery would be returned by the power lessees. The remainder would be amortized over a fifty-year period at 4 percent interest.[10]

Before construction could begin, the act required the secretary of the interior to secure contracts for the sale of hydroelectric power. These agreements were to generate revenue sufficient to repay the costs of the dam and power plant within fifty years. Part of this provision irritated Mead. To compensate for the taxes they could collect from privately owned facilities, Arizona and Nevada each were given 18¾ percent of surplus power revenues. Mead considered this arrangement "vicious" and "extorted from the needs of California." He saw no justification for giving these two states special privileges "for allowing others to use the water flowing to the sea past their boundary and which nature prevents their using." Later, when power rates were being determined, Arizona and Nevada tried to have them set high so they could reap greater returns, but Mead thwarted their efforts. The contracts established a unit price for hydroelectric energy at the minimum levels required for the government to be repaid, as the act required. Power lessees agreed to operate and maintain the power plant and to repay the cost of the plant's equipment within ten years.[11]

While these contracts were being negotiated, U.S. representatives began talks with Mexico on mutual water issues. In 1924, Mead had been appointed chairman of the American section of the International Water Commission, empowered to negotiate a distribution of the waters of the Rio Grande, Colorado, and Tijuana rivers. A settlement was complicated by the need of American farmers on the lower Rio Grande for water from that stream's Mexican tributaries and by Mexican farmers' use of "American" water from the lower Colorado. In the mid-1920s, when Mexico increased development of her lands along rivers feeding the Rio Grande, Texas farmers became alarmed. They feared that their interests might be sacrificed for a Colorado settlement, while those persons concerned with the Colorado Basin feared a favorable Rio Grande agreement at their expense. As the Boulder Canyon project proceeded, Mead's primary concern was the Imperial Valley's dependence on Mexico for an anticipated eight years until the dam and canal were completed. Representatives of the two countries began formal talks in August 1929, after almost five years of gathering information.[12]

As head of the U.S. delegation, Mead skillfully presented his case. He tried to convince the Mexican representatives of the flood- and silt-control benefits their country would derive from American improvements on the Colorado, but when he only offered up to one million acre-feet of water they rejected it as totally inadequate. The United States refused further concessions on the Colorado so the Mexicans would not budge on the Rio Grande. The discussions became deadlocked. Mead then sought an agreement on flood control alone. He regarded settlement on water allotment as desirable but not essential at that time. Serious injury to Mexico lay in the future, and the United States would continue its development regardless. On the other hand, he feared that the irrigated lands in both countries were in jeopardy until the Colorado construction was finished and ensured "a safe and permanent regimen for the river." The talks broke off, however, with nothing achieved on this point. Fortunately, no serious flood threat developed along the lower basin while the Colorado River project was being built.[13]

Plans for construction began even before President Coolidge signed the act in December 1928. In May of that year, Congress authorized a five-man committee to inspect the proposed sites for the dam and to study "the safety, economic and engineering feasibility, and adequacy of the proposed structure." Construction would begin when this group, known as the Colorado River Board, approved the plans. The members included three engineers—Major General William L. Sibert (retired), as chairman; Daniel W. Mead; and Robert Ridgeway—and two geologists, Charles F. Berkey and Warren J. Mead. (The Meads were not related to the commissioner.) After careful study, the board recommended raising the height of the proposed dam by 25 feet—to 727 feet—for more effective flood control. They also examined the possible sites for the dam in Boulder and Black canyons, and made a detailed report on the advantages and problems of each location.[14]

In June 1929, Mead, Secretary of the Interior Wilbur, and a contingent of engineers made an inspection tour of the canyons. After careful consideration, they selected a location for the dam in Black Canyon, its access from Las Vegas being an important factor in the choice. The exact details of design and plans for construction then began in earnest. While engineering specifications were prepared, work proceeded on the logistical problems of moving huge quantities of material to the site and erecting housing for the large number of men who would build the dam. On July 4, 1930, Wilbur ordered Mead to commence construction. Soon thereafter, the Union Pacific Railroad laid a twenty-three-mile line from Las Vegas, while Nevada built a highway the same distance. Both of these transportation facilities terminated at the construction reservation; the government, and later the contractors, completed the road and railway to the site.[15]

The dam was built in a remote section of the country, necessitating special consideration for the comforts of the men who would work in the area. This problem particularly concerned Mead, and when the delegation inspected the site for the dam in June 1929, he picked out a location high above the heat of the canyon floor to erect the needed housing. Because the construction was expected to take eight years, Interior Department officials agreed that substantial facilities were essential. Mead preferred to go beyond this and build a permanent town. He believed the dam and the lake that would form behind it would prove to be a tourist attraction, drawing thousands of visitors each year. Servicing the tourists and the staff that would run the dam and power plant would provide the future economic base for the town.[16]

Mead's vision of the future proved to be correct, but his immediate concern was the creation of surroundings conducive to the well-being and efficiency of the workers. He wanted to provide "not only sanitary and comfortable living accommodations," but conditions which would make for "sobriety and a clean moral atmosphere." He wanted the government to maintain close control over who would be permitted in the vicinity of the construction site. In this way, he hoped to keep out such disruptive influences as gamblers, prostitutes, bootleggers, and, presumably, labor agitators. Moreover, the commissioner was determined that speculators would not build a "boom town" and make excessive profits off the workers. Accordingly, he persuaded Secretary Wilbur of the need to establish a government reservation, and Congress authorized almost two million dollars—as part of the cost of the dam—to provide facilities for the workers. The Reclamation Bureau hired a town planner, and he laid out a fan-shaped community that was named Boulder City.[17]

Although this arrangement had advantages, it caused a great deal of controversy. Mead spent an undue amount of time in overseeing details of the town's operations and defending what went on there. Nevada officials regarded the establishment of the reservation as an encroachment on the state's sovereignty, while Las Vegas merchants objected because the contractors of the dam were required to have 80 percent of their employees live in Boulder City. The state brought suit, and in order to end the litigation and proceed with construction the federal government abandoned attempts to exercise exclusive control in perpetuity. Instead, the Bureau of Reclamation retained title to land in the reservation area only until the dam was completed. Meanwhile, because a person would be leasing land in the town or surrounding territory, the federal government could regulate closely the "proper conduct" of concessionaires, and as owner of the land exclude undesirables from the property. Law officers were both federal marshals and deputy sheriffs of Mohave County, able to administer whichever law was applicable.[18]

Boulder City was established to eliminate the worst features of the "company town." It had definite positive features, the most important being that it provided a clean, essentially vice-free atmosphere at reasonable rates for the majority of the construction crew. But it was not without faults. Sims Ely, the city manager, was attacked often, and with apparently some justification, for the dictatorial and arbitrary way he performed his duties. Moreover, Six Companies, Incorporated, the chief builders of the dam, set up a subsidiary enterprise to operate concessions in the town, and appeared to take advantage of their favored position by thwarting competition. For example, they issued private script to employees until 1933, when, after numerous protests, Secretary Ickes ordered them to cease the practice. In addition, there was a constant barrage of complaints about inadequate facilities, especially during the early period of the dam's construction.[19]

Part of the problem with Boulder City stemmed from the depression. Before housing for the workers could be completed, construction of the dam began. In the fall of 1930, President Hoover requested that the work assist in relieving unemployment by proceeding with the "utmost dispatch possible." Mead ordered his engineers to speed plans and specifications, and bids were let in December, six months ahead of schedule. Men began flocking to southern Nevada in search of jobs soon after the contract was signed on March 11, 1931.[20]

The general contract was awarded to Six Companies, Incorporated, a consortium of construction firms organized to bid on this project. In 1929 Mead had suggested to Interior Secretary Wilbur that, because of the restricted space in the canyon, one contractor handle the building of the dam. He felt that a number of smaller construction companies would be in each other's way, require duplication of machinery, and add to the cost of the structure. Six Companies offered to build the dam for 48,890,995 dollars, less than one-twentieth of 1 percent over the confidential estimate of the Bureau of Reclamation, and 5 million dollars lower than the nearest competitor.[21]

The terms of the contract called for Six Companies to build cofferdams upstream and downstream for diversion of the river, to drill four tunnels fifty-feet in diameter to reroute the stream past the construction site, and to erect the huge concrete dam. As the government would supply all permanent materials for the structure, the contract, in effect, required the company to furnish the men, machinery, and management needed to build the dam. Mead set up a special section in the bureau under Raymond F. Walter as chief engineer and Walker R. Young as construction engineer to coordinate the overall direction of the project. Mead had complete confidence in both men, and thus was free for other administrative duties and free from day-to-day problems. Nevertheless, the entire undertaking was his responsibility, and he kept a close watch on the details of the massive project, paying particular attention to the operations of Boulder City, his final attempt at a model community.[22]

Six Companies began work in May 1931 and by July 4, when they started to excavate the diversion tunnels, had over two thousand men employed. Work proceeded steadily until August 7, when a strike temporarily halted construction. A misunderstanding over wages triggered the walkout, but the underlying cause was basic discontentment over living and working conditions. This was before Boulder City was completed, and most of the workers were living in Williamsville (also called Ragtown), a temporary ramshackle tent community on the floor of the canyon. Six Companies, moreover, had not completed arrangements for such necessities as ice water for men toiling in temperatures up to 120 degrees. Mead blamed the situation on the haste with which the project was begun in order to help relieve the acute unemployment on the Pacific Coast.[23]

The commissioner was dismayed at the attacks on his bureau in the nation's press. He vigorously defended the Six Companies, pointing to the money that was being spent to provide a decent atmosphere for the employees. Admitting that there were valid complaints, he noted that problems were being corrected as rapidly as possible. Meanwhile, somewhat heavy-handedly, Walker R. Young, the construction engineer, ordered the striking men off the reservation on August 11. Two days later, they returned to work.[24]

In the spring of 1932, another problem arose when several congressmen wrote to Secretary Wilbur about discrimination in the hiring of blacks. Only two blacks—both bootblacks—were allowed in the reservation, and they had to return to Las Vegas twenty-two miles away each night. This was at a time when over three thousand men were working on the dam. Mead and Wilbur took the position that the government could not force the companies to hire blacks because the requirement was not in their contracts. Mead noted the difficulties of housing and feeding "colored labor," and the cost of providing separate facilities. He feared serious disruption if they were integrated in the dormitories and eating halls. Nevertheless, Six Companies volunteered to hire blacks. It was a mere token gesture. By October 1933, sixty-five had been hired, mostly for roadwork. In September, Ickes issued orders that there would be no discrimination in Boulder City. This, too, was essentially meaningless; in the spring of 1934, a mere 11 blacks were working in a total force of over 4,500.[25]

Employment peaked in the summer of 1934 at almost five thousand workers while the dam structure was poured. Drilling the diversion tunnels had proceeded so rapidly in 1932 that Mead revised the schedule and asked Congress for additional appropriations to accelerate the construction of the cofferdams to block the river and turn the water into the tunnels. The work had to be done in the fall and winter when the Colorado's flow was low. Appealing to a penurious Congress, Mead stressed the loss in power revenue from a year's delay if the cofferdams were not completed by the spring of 1933. He also pointed to the hardships the workers would experience if stranded in the desert for a year as construction lagged. The money request was granted.[26]

Once the cofferdams were in place, workers stripped the canyon to bedrock, and on June 6, 1933, they poured the first sixteen-ton bucket of concrete. For almost two years, this process was repeated every two minutes, twenty-four hours a day. The dam, 660 feet thick at the base, tapered to 45 feet at the top as it rose over 725 feet. Constructed in huge blocks, the structure was laced with 662 miles of copper tubing through which ice water flowed, allowing it to stay cool and dry evenly. (Had it been poured solidly, it would have been plagued with huge cracks and required 125 years to dry.) By the time the last bucket was emptied, some 6,900,000 tons of concrete had been used.[27]

The round-the-clock construction schedule that enabled the speedy completion of the dam was not without problems. When the Public Works Administration took over the financing of the dam in 1933, for example, one PWA regulation limited the amount of time a person could work to thirty hours a week. Mead argued that applying this rule to the Boulder Canyon project would increase construction costs and benefit no one. There was nothing for men to do in that remote section of the country except work. Their wages would be cut because of the shortened week, but their living expenses could not be reduced proportionately. (They were working fifty-six hours a week.) Moreover, Six Companies would have to build many more facilities for employees who would have to be hired for only a short time. PWA officials accepted his reasoning and exempted the Boulder Canyon project from the thirty-hour provision.[28]

For nearly two years, construction flowed as freely as did the concrete. In February 1935, however, a new problem arose when

Justice Department agents seized the Six Companies' records and accused them of more than seventy thousand violations of the eight-hour-day law. Mead was upset at the action, which he felt discredited the Interior Department and the contractors. He defended the contractors and told Ickes that Six Companies, from the beginning, had been "straight forward and honest." Henry Kaiser, president of Six Companies, was indignant at the charges and the proposed fine of 5 dollars per violation. After considerable communication, the government deducted 100,000 dollars from a payment to the contractors and Six Companies acquiesced without acknowledging culpability.[29]

Another difficulty occurred on July 13, 1935, when a strike, the second one during the construction period, temporarily halted work. By this time the operation was being cut back from three shifts to one shift a day. Employees had been paid for 8 hours but worked 7½, with 30 minutes allotted for lunch. Now Six Companies wanted 8 hours of labor exclusive of lunch. The men objected to this. They also wanted a cut to a 48-hour workweek as well as a pay hike. Wages had been set when the contract was let in 1931, so an adjustment clearly seemed to be in order. Mead favored an increase because he felt that it was justified and because he wanted nothing to interfere with the completion of the dam. After a series of hastily held conferences, the companies conceded the first two points and an arbitration panel compromised on pay. The men returned to work on July 26.[30]

Mead was as genuinely concerned about the welfare of the workers as he had been about the settlers on reclamation projects. They had done a wonderful job, he appreciated their efforts, and he was interested in their future. In 1934, he proposed having those who were laid off as the dam neared completion moved to other projects. He thought the training and expertise the workers had gained would be especially valuable at Grand Coulee Dam, the second huge multipurpose project that the Reclamation Bureau was undertaking. But Mead's superiors in the Interior Department ruled against a mass movement of laborers to another area. They told him, however, that there was "no reason why men laid off . . . could not return home or any locality in which they wished to settle."[31]

Many workers discharged from the Boulder Dam project found employment on the construction of the All-American Canal being built west of the Imperial Dam, seventeen miles above Yuma, Arizona. In May 1933, Mead had asked Secretary Ickes to begin the canal as soon as possible, stressing that the construction would aid in relieving unemployment. He also warned Ickes that unless it was finished about the same time as Boulder Dam, Mexico might expand her irrigated croplands with the regulated flow of the Colorado. This would establish a right under international law to the water's continued use. Complications in securing contracts with the Coachella District water users delayed the letting of contracts, however, and canal construction did not begin until August 1935.[32]

In that year, the number of men employed on Boulder Dam in Black Canyon began a precipitate decline. On February 1, workers closed one portal and a lake began to form behind the 727-foot arch-shaped concrete structure. As the finishing touches on the dam and power plant continued, plans for a formal dedication were made. By this time, Secretary Ickes had become thoroughly disenchanted with Mead, whom he found entirely too independent. The president insisted that Mead be part of the official party, but Ickes saw to it that he would not have a speaking role. His efforts were wasted. On September 30, President Franklin D. Roosevelt presided over the festivities at Boulder Dam. It was an impressive ceremony, attended by six governors, many high government officials, and twelve thousand visitors. The activities were marred by the absence of one notable figure. At the official dedication of his crowning achievement, Dr. Elwood Mead lay ill in a Los Angeles hospital.[33]

By October Mead had recuperated from his illness and had

gone back to work, but he was feeling his age. After his return to Washington, he continued at his job until a stroke felled him a few days after his seventy-eighth birthday. He lingered about a week, and died on January 26, 1936. Ten days later Secretary of the Interior Ickes announced that the reservoir forming behind Boulder Dam—Mead's last and largest achievement—would be named Lake Mead in honor of the deceased Commissioner of Reclamation.[34]

TEN

Conclusion

FOR OVER FIFTY YEARS, ELWOOD MEAD DEVOTED his life to the problems of irrigation and irrigators. His career paralleled the rise to maturity of reclamation in the United States. When he arrived in the West in 1882, irrigation as a cooperative venture was coming to an end. Until then, several farmers would construct a diversion ditch and water the lowlands along a stream. It was a simple operation: the water users invested no money— only time and a few materials that usually they found in the area. At the time of his death in 1936, Mead had just finished directing the construction of a 100 million dollar multipurpose dam that took almost five thousand men five years to erect. Five million barrels of cement, eight million tons of sand, and massive quantities of other materials went into the giant structure.

Engineering feats and construction statistics are only part of the story of Elwood Mead's contributions to the conquest of arid lands around the world. Mead had an international reputation as an irrigation engineer, but he looked beyond the technological aspects of dam and canal building. To him, the reclaiming of desert lands was more than an engineering problem; it encompassed all aspects of putting the land to use and settling it with family farmers.

Mead's interest in securing resident farmers was rooted in his youth. As he grew up in Indiana, he saw an idyllic agrarian community spoiled by the infusion of tenants who leased land from speculators. At the same time, he was blessed with his grandfather's library. Reading widened his world and sharpened his criticism of the drab country existence. Although he loved farming, he came to hate rural life. Mead's dislike did not turn to scorn, however; he was imbued with a belief in the blessings of farm life. Instead of rejecting the countryside, he sought to transform and mold it into a desirable social and economic entity.

In college, Mead majored in agriculture. After graduation, he accepted a teaching position in Colorado, where he came into contact with irrigation farming. He returned to the Midwest only for a brief period, picking up a graduate degree in civil engineering and a knowledge of law. With this unique combination of training, he spent the rest of his life working for the betterment of rural society. His specific concern was irrigation farming, which offered a challenge in his two fields of interest—agriculture and engineering.

When Mead arrived at Fort Collins, Colorado, irrigation in the West was beginning to change from individual to large-scale operations. The state was struggling with the problems of regulating its limited supply of water. As Mead observed this phenomenon, it challenged his most basic principles. Already speculators had entered the field, and Mead viewed their activities as akin to the ruinous practices that had driven him from his Indiana farm. More than this, his engineering and legal training had instilled in him a passion for orderliness—things should follow prescribed rules. Finally, from his undergraduate days, when he had to work and go to school, he developed the habit of utilizing his time to maximum efficiency. He carried this trait throughout his life, and applied it to everything. He hated waste. In Colorado, the three characteristics that molded Mead's attitude toward his life's work—love of farming, of order, and of efficiency—were threatened at every turn. Speculation was widespread, the laws chaotic, and water wasted. Although in no position to affect conditions in Colorado significantly, he studied the problems of irrigation and formulated solutions to deal with them. As he aired his views, he gained a reputation as something of an expert on irrigation.

When Wyoming officials began to deal with the problems of water distribution, they consulted the Colorado professor, and then hired him as territorial engineer. At last, Mead had the opportunity to test his ideas. In 1890, when Wyoming became a state, he wrote its water code and devised the system to administer it. These innovations served as a model for most states in the American West as well as in Australia, New Zealand, South Africa, and Canada. It was a significant contribution to the arid regions of the world. Wyoming's water laws followed a logical arrangement that ended conflicts over rights and gave order to the distribution of the water supply.

To Mead, distribution was a first step toward realizing the full potential of irrigation. After the water was divided, it had to be applied to the land. The law required that it be appropriated "for beneficial use," which Mead regarded as more than a convenient application of water. It implied using the water in the most efficient manner for the most effective results.

The efficient use of water encompassed two ideas. From a social standpoint, it meant providing agricultural opportunities for small farmers; from an engineering standpoint, it meant regulating the flow of streams to obtain maximum benefit from the available supply. In Wyoming, for example, Mead sought to combine a small plot of irrigated land with a larger area of grazing land so that more people would have a financial base to succeed as farmers. He wanted the federal lands in the West ceded to the states who would lease them for grazing. The proceeds would be used to finance irrigation works needed to regulate the rivers for greatest effect.

In the early 1890s, Mead opposed federal involvement in irrigation, and only reluctantly, after the Carey Act proved to be a disappointment, did he advocate a limited role for the federal government. He believed that, for the most part, the states were better qualified to direct the development of resources within their boundaries, and the federal government should become involved only in the construction of large reservoirs for stream regulation. Mead opposed a large-scale building program directed from Washington, an attitude that put him in disfavor with the proponents of a national reclamation policy. He predicted unfavorable consequences and urged a cautious approach, but his warnings were not heeded. With passage of the Reclamation Act of 1902, the federal government was in the reclamation business.

While federal construction proceeded, Mead, who had been shunted aside, did what he could to assist irrigation farmers. As head of irrigation investigations for the Agriculture Department from 1898 to 1907, he offered advice and instruction to the small cultivator. A long series of bulletins were the result of experimentation with crops, varieties of seeds, and methods of irrigation, all designed to aid farmers in the most productive and profitable utilization of their lands. Interdepartmental bickering frustrated his efforts, but he persevered for five years after the passage of the Reclamation Act. Mead had only a small role in the government and virtually no say in policy, but in a modest way he helped to ameliorate some of the problems of the irrigator.

As Mead's frustrations in Washington increased, his ideas attracted the attention of President Benjamin Ide Wheeler of the University of California. Concerned that his institution was not doing enough in the area of irrigation, Wheeler convinced Mead to return to the classroom. He taught under a part-time arrangement for several years, but about the time Mead was ready to accept a regular professorship at Berkeley the 1906 earthquake hit San Francisco. Subsequent budget constraints prevented him from being offered the kind of salary he might otherwise have commanded, so he looked elsewhere.

In 1907, officials in the state of Victoria, Australia, asked Mead to come there to help with a variety of water problems. A six-month interlude turned into an eight-year stay during which his ideas matured about what should be done to revitalize rural life. He found "down under" a progressive government, unshackled by rigid traditions against state action, willing to experiment with ways to improve the general welfare of its citizens.

Mead took the Australian practice of closer settlements and applied it to irrigated lands. The reclaimed areas made it possible to bring in immigrants to farm, a critical need for the economic development of Australia. The increased population added to the wealth of the country, thus justifying the government's expenditures for reclamation. And as an added bonus, the plan provided a way to extricate Victoria from the huge investment it had made in irrigation facilities.

When Mead returned to the United States in 1915, he was enthusiastic about the benefits of so-called state paternalism, especially as he had applied it to reclamation. He wanted to demonstrate in his native country the planned rural community that he saw as so successful for the development of Victoria. Despite many avowed backers of the plan, however, it was never received with much enthusiasm in America.

The reasons for the lack of support were simple, but Mead never seemed to recognize them. In Australia, immigration was promoted actively by the government. The newcomers were channeled to the countryside because of the strength of the Labour party and the need to build the rural economy. Since good farmland was scarce, irrigation was necessary to create a place for the immigrants. In short, government policy encouraged rural development. The United States, on the other hand, was moving toward immigration restriction, and its energies were being directed to urbanization and industrialization. All the good lands had been taken, and few people outside the West felt the need to "create" more. With the rural population in decline and the rise of the city, conditions in America were almost diametrically opposite those in Australia.

There were people, however, who saw compelling reasons to try Mead's ideas for planned rural communities. Many progressives, motivated like Mead by the nostalgia of the agrarian idyll, supported the scheme. Some argued for expanded farm opportunities as an antidote to unemployment, as an alternative to the "evils" of the city, and later as a reward to ex-servicemen. Mead promoted rural colonies on a national level before and after World War I. He came closest to success when he tried to make the plan a bonus for veterans, but opposition, especially from agricultural groups, blocked the passage of land-settlement measures.

In California, Mead secured legislation in 1917 and 1919 to found two model rural communities. Durham, the first of these "demonstration" colonies, began under favorable circumstances: especially high farm prices and enough applicants to allow selectivity. Its apparent success led to a second settlement at Delhi. By the time it opened for occupancy, however, war-inflated farm prices had dropped and the number of persons interested in farming had fallen as well. Solvency at Delhi was maintained as long as state money for a drainage system supplemented the income of the farmers. When the funds were discontinued, the colony almost collapsed. After settlers were granted special favors there, Durham residents demanded the same. Both colonies ended in failure.

Mead blamed the Durham and Delhi debacle primarily on Governor Richardson, but the fault was more than politics and even deeper than the agricultural depression of the 1920s. Although state-aided and directed settlement had many excellent features, it had several serious flaws as well. One drawback was that, compared to private schemes, it gave the settlers special advantages. Mead had observed how preferential treatment in federal reclamation opened the door to more and more concessions and threat-

ened to make water users "wards" of the state. He never seemed
to recognize that this same consequence applied to his own scheme.
Moreover, the plan tended to infringe on the time-honored farmer
tradition of independence. The Land Settlement Board gave direction and controlled the aid; settlers found it advisable to do what
was "recommended" if they expected financial assistance. It was a
short step from direction to dictatorship.

After he became Commissioner of Reclamation, Mead continued
to advocate his plan on a national level, but he was unsuccessful in
both the irrigated lands of the West and the cutover and swampy
areas of the South. However, his basic concept finally saw fruition
in the Subsistence Homesteads Program of the New Deal. Its or-
ganizers acknowledged Mead's influence both for the theory and
for the years he had promoted planned community settlements.

His ideas on community development also took Mead abroad
in the 1920s. He was invited to return to Australia, where soldier
settlement schemes for World War I veterans were foundering.
Despite his advice (or perhaps because of it), these colonies, like
Durham and Delhi, ended in costly failure. Likewise, his recommendations for Hawaiian natives resulted in minimal success.
Only in Palestine, where a unique combination of circumstances
provided an ideal background to test his theories, did things appear to turn out well. He correctly perceived the role the *kibbutzim*
would play in Israel's history, and he made invaluable suggestions
to help direct it toward that end.

Mead, of course, had promoted his plans in this country primarily in connection with irrigation, although he envisioned the
community idea eventually spreading to all of rural America. He
was never able to show convincingly the necessity for such measures, nor were many of his other views readily accepted. For example, he had always been wary of federal involvement in reclamation and had urged a cautious building program when the
Reclamation Act was passed in 1902. Before long, officials of the
Reclamation Service found themselves confronted with the evils

Mead had feared—overbuilding, land speculation, and disgruntled settlers demanding special treatment.

The Reclamation Act had been based on the dual assumption that the land reclaimed would go to actual settlers and that the cost of reclamation would be repaid by those who benefited. To Mead, these two precepts were the only justification for government involvement. In practice, neither supposition was fulfilled. Problems plagued the Reclamation Service from its beginning. Difficulties stemmed from the haste with which projects were begun and from the political necessity to build facilities in every state in the West. Twice Mead was called upon to assess the deteriorating state of affairs and make recommendations. World War I temporarily alleviated the 1916 situation. When things worsened again in the 1920s, Mead was asked to help reorient federal reclamation to fit the role envisioned by its original supporters.

As a member of the Fact Finders Committee, Mead played a key part in formulating a new policy for reclamation. As Commissioner of Reclamation, he directed the implementation of that policy. Under his leadership, federal reclamation underwent a thorough reordering. His was a "business" approach, but it was not legalistic. He insisted that water users meet their obligations to the government, but he also insisted that those debts be legitimate—water users ought not pay for the government's mistakes. At the same time, he initiated changes to decentralize reclamation by giving the water users control of their irrigation facilities and the responsibility for operating them—to get the government out of reclamation as much as possible.

By 1926 Mead had set the Reclamation Bureau on a new path. Through the changes he introduced, the financial position of federal reclamation showed a steady and substantial improvement until the Great Depression. Even during that period of severe economic difficulties, federal reclamation was on a more solid base than most enterprises; the moratoriums on construction repayments, for example, were necessary for only five years.

Additionally, Mead was determined to avoid a repetition of the problems that stemmed from inadequate planning. He insisted that no new projects begin until investigations showed their feasibility and until there were assurances that the facilities would benefit actual farmers, albeit with less than total success. He also launched a long-range program to complete facilities on partially developed projects. This work put the Bureau in an excellent position to aid in the economic recovery of the country through the public works projects of the New Deal. The Reclamation Bureau was ready to begin a massive building program as soon as funds were appropriated.

The largest project directed by Mead as Commissioner of Reclamation was the construction of Boulder Dam on the Colorado River. It was also the most carefully planned undertaking the Bureau had ever attempted; years went into the preparations for the giant structure. Mead had primary responsibility for its overall direction and assembled an excellent staff to handle the operations. Still, he took an active role, especially in areas of direct interest to himself. For example, Mead was concerned about the welfare of the workers on the remote, hot, and dangerous construction site. He attempted to provide living conditions to make their task as comfortable as possible.

Boulder City was Mead's final attempt at a model community. He planned it not only for the construction period, but also as a town for tourists and the permanent employees of the dam and power plant. In some ways, his vision of it for the future proved to be more successful than its prime purpose of serving the workers during the building of the dam. However, the town's problems were not so much Mead's fault as they were the result of the haste in beginning construction to relieve unemployment and a certain amount of greed on the part of the Six Companies.

Despite the problems that arose over Boulder City, construction of the dam moved at a remarkable pace. Finished two years ahead of schedule, the giant concrete structure was a tribute to Mead's organizing genius—and it was fitting that the sprawling lake that formed behind the dam was named in his honor.

It is somewhat ironic that Mead, who in the 1890s had opposed federal involvement in reclamation, should direct the construction of the largest reclamation project in America. Mead had firm convictions, but he was not dogmatic. His whole life showed a constant adjustment to new realities. If his warnings had been heeded, the federal government would not have become so deeply entrenched in reclamation, or, at least not in such a haphazard fashion. Once it did become involved, however, Mead sought to ensure that it would achieve its original purpose—helping men own farms.

Mead's paramount concern was the welfare of the common man—the small farmer who formed the backbone of the world he envisioned. He was a public servant, not just a government employee. As his ideas evolved, he came to accept a larger and larger role for the government in reclamation, but only as it provided expanded opportunities for the average citizen. To hasten the realization of this goal, he strove to apply the principles of engineering to community planning. In promoting agrarian ideals through technological advances, Elwood Mead attempted to secure the betterment of society by combining the best from the past with the hopes of the future. Unfortunately, he failed to see his dream fulfilled.

Notes

Chapter 1

1. Elwood Mead to his son, Thomas C. Mead, n.d., Thomas Chase Mead Papers, in possession of T. C. Mead, Boulder City, Nevada (hereafter cited as T. C. Mead Papers); Elwood Mead to F. L. Sanford, March 8, 1923, carton 3, Elwood Mead Correspondence and Papers, Bancroft Library, University of California, Berkeley (hereafter cited as Mead Papers); interview with Thomas Mead, January 3, 1970, Boulder City, Nevada; Daniel Mead entry, Switzerland County, Indiana, Eighth Census of the United States, 1860, National Archives.

2. Thomas Mead interview, January 3, 1970; Perret Dufour, *The Swiss Settlement of Switzerland County, Indiana* (Indianapolis: Indiana Historical Commission, 1925), 1–9.

3. Thomas Mead interview, January 3, 1970.

4. Ibid.; Emma Lou Thornbrough, *Indiana in the Civil War Era, 1850–1880* (Indianapolis: Indiana Historical Bureau and Indiana Historical Society, 1965), 203.

5. Elwood Mead to Jennie A. Bristol, March 4, 1923, and Elwood Mead address, "The Meeting of Orientals and Occidentals in the Pacific Coast Area," August 11, 1920, cartons 3, 12, Mead Papers. Elwood Mead, "Rural Life in America," *The American Review of Reviews* 73 (March 1926): 303.

6. Elwood Mead, "Meeting of Orientals and Occidentals," carton 12, Mead Papers; Elwood Mead, "Community Farming," *The New Republic* 41 (February 18, 1925): 327.

7. Thomas Mead interview, January 3, 1970; R. F. Walter and William H. Code, with the assistance of Frank Adams, "Elwood Mead, M. Am. Soc. C.E." *American Society of Civil Engineers Transactions* 102 (1937): 1617.

8. Ibid.; Paul K. Conkin, "The Vision of Elwood Mead," *Agricultural History* 34 (April 1960): 88; William Hepburn, *Purdue University: Fifty Years of Progress* (Lafayette, Ind.: Purdue University Press, 1924), 65.

9. Thomas Mead interview, January 3, 1970.

10. Ibid.; Hepburn, *Purdue University,* 67–69; Clifton J. Phillips, *Indiana in Transition: The Emergence of an Industrial Commonwealth, 1880–1920* (Indianapolis: Indiana Historical Bureau and Indiana Historical Society, 1968), 142–43; Elwood Mead, "Tobacco" (handwritten thesis in Agriculture), Purdue University, Thesis no. 30, 1882.

11. Secretary of War to Secretary of Interior, May 8, 1928, file 22–63 [Elwood Mead], Appointments Division, Department of Interior [ADDI], record group 48, National Archives; Mead to C. E. Nordyke, April 3, 1922, carton 1, Mead Papers; James R. Miller, "Pioneer College Presidents," typescript (1962), 184, Colorado State University, Fort Collins.

12. Ruth J. Wattles, "The Mile High College: A History of Colorado A and M" (typescript, n.d.), 25, Colorado State University, Fort Collins. There was no regular assistant state engineer at this time. The state engineer hired local engineers for specific jobs as needed. *Second Biennial Report of the State Engineer of the State of Colorado, 1883–1884* (Denver: Collier and Cleaveland Lith. Co., 1885), 5.

13. Robert G. Dunbar, "The Origins of the Colorado System of Water-Right Control," *The Colorado Magazine* 27 (October 1950): 241–45, and his "Water Conflicts and Controls in Colorado," *Agricultural History* 22 (July 1948): 180–86; Ralph Hess, "The Beginnings of Irrigation in the U.S.", *Political Economy* 20 (October 1912): 827–28; David Boyd, *Greeley and the Union Colony of Colorado* (Greeley, Colo.: Greeley Tribune Press, 1890), 88–141; Alvin T. Steinel and D. W. Working, *History of Agriculture in Colorado* (Fort Collins, Colo.: State Agricultural College, 1926), 395–96.

14. Dunbar, "Origins of the Colorado System," 244–45, 251–62; Elwood Mead, *Irrigation Institutions* (New York: Macmillan Company, 1903), 143. For a provocative discussion of the background to the Colo-

rado system, see Donald J. Pisani, "Enterprise and Equity: A Critique of Western Water Law in the Nineteenth Century," *Western Historical Quarterly* 18 (January 1987): 15–37.

15. Wattles, "Mile High College," 11, 16.

16. Ibid., 8–9.

17. Ibid., 9, 27; Mead to E. B. House, February 24, 1922, carton 1, Mead Papers.

18. Ibid.; Thomas Mead interview, January 3, 1970; newspaper article, n.d., T. C. Mead Papers; Iowa State University archivist Dorothy Kehlenbeck to author, February 24, 1970.

19. *Third Biennial Report of the State Engineer of the State of Colorado, 1885–1886* (Denver: Collier and Cleaveland Lith. Co., 1887), 6; Wattles, "Mile High College," 9–10.

20. Wattles, "Mile High College," 9, 27; Elwood Mead, "Recollections of Irrigation Legislation in Wyoming," typescript, with letter to Grace Raymond Hebard, March 27, 1930, Heberd Collection, Western History Research Center, University of Wyoming, Laramie; Elwood Mead to E. B. House, February 24, 1922, carton 1, Mead Papers.

21. Robert G. Dunbar, *Forging New Rights in Western Waters* (Lincoln: University of Nebraska Press, 1983), 101–4.

22. Elwood Mead, *The Ownership of Water* (Denver: Times Printing Works, 1887), 5–8.

23. Ibid., 4–5.

24. Steinel and Working, *History of Agriculture in Colorado,* 221.

Chapter 2

1. Taft A. Larson, *History of Wyoming* (Lincoln: University of Nebraska Press, 1965), 190–94.

2. Ibid., 150, 153–58, 162; Lewis L. Gould, *Wyoming: A Political History, 1868–1896* (New Haven: Yale University Press, 1968), 100, 106; Elwood Mead, "Recollections of Irrigation Legislation in Wyoming," Heberd Collection. See also W. Turrentine Jackson, "Administration of Thomas Moonlight, 1887–89," *Annals of Wyoming* 18 (July 1946): 139–62.

3. Elwood Mead, "Recollections of Irrigation Legislation in Wyo-

ming"; W. E. Chaplin, "Memoir of the Constitutional Convention"; and William C. Deming, unidentified newspaper article, Hebard Collection. [Wyoming Constitutional Convention], typescript dated June 10, 1925, file 22-63, ADDI; Thomas Moonlight to Elwood Mead, March 12, 1888, Letterpress books of the Governors, 1869–1907, Wyoming State Archives and Historical Department, Cheyenne.

4. Mead, *Irrigation Institutions,* 249; Mead to Moonlight, November 10, 1888, typescript, State Engineer's Office, Cheyenne, Wyoming [SEOW]; [Wyoming Constitutional Convention], file 22–63, ADDI.

5. Mead to Moonlight, November 10, 1888, SEOW.

6. Ibid.; Mead, "Recollections of Irrigation Legislation in Wyoming," Heberd Collection; Frank Adams, "Irrigation, Reclamation and Water Administration" (oral history conducted 1958), Regional Oral History Office, University of California, Berkeley [ROHOUC], 86.

7. Mead, "Recollections of Irrigation Legislation in Wyoming," Hebard Collection; Mead to Moonlight, November 10, 1888, SEOW; Adams interview, ROHOUC, 85–86; Mead, *Irrigation Institutions,* 249.

8. Mead, "Recollections of Irrigation Legislation in Wyoming," Hebard Collection; Mead to Moonlight, November 10, 1888, SEOW; Mead, *Irrigation Institutions,* 250–51.

9. Mead to Moonlight, November 10, 1888, SEOW.

10. Gould, *Wyoming,* 112–13.

11. Chaplin, "Memoir of the Constitutional Convention"; Mead, "Recollections of Irrigation Legislation in Wyoming"; unidentified newspaper articles from time of convention, Hebard Collection. Mead to John A. Whiting, October 27, 1931, file 143–53, General Correspondence, Reclamation Bureau [GCRB], record group 115, National Archives. *Journals and Debates of the Constitutional Convention of the State of Wyoming* (Cheyenne: The Daily Sun, 1893), 497–512, 534–37. Lewis L. Gould, *History of Wyoming* (Lincoln: University of Nebraska Press, 1978), 254–55.

12. *Constitution of the State of Wyoming,* Article 8. *Second Annual Report of the Territorial Engineer of Wyoming, 1889* (Cheyenne: Bristol and Knabe Printing Company, 1890), 91. Among the waters that came under the control of the state engineer were the Hot Springs in the Big Horn Mountains, now in Thermopolis. They are used as medicinal baths.

13. *Second Annual Report,* 96–99; Mead, *Irrigation Institutions,* 266–71. Mead, "Recollections of Irrigation Legislation in Wyoming," Hebard Collection; Mead to Whiting, October 27, 1931, file 143-53, GRRB. Mead sometimes carried regulations to an extreme. He wrote one farmer that his plat was unacceptable because it was not to a two-inch scale, and because of its appearance: "It is of importance to you that it should not only be correct, but should also impress the board. This will hardly be the case with a plat made with a lead pencil and defaced with writing and figures on the back." Mead to W. E. Grimes, November 5, 1891, State Engineer's Correspondence, Wyoming State Archives and Historical Department, Cheyenne [SECWA].

14. Mead, "Recollections of Irrigation Legislation in Wyoming," Hebard Collection. *Second Annual Report,* 93–95; Mead, *Irrigation Institutions,* 252–66.

15. Adams interview, ROHOUC, 89. *Second Biennial Report of the State Engineer of Wyoming, 1893–1894* (Cheyenne: Bristol and Knabe Printing Company, 1895), 16; Mead, *Irrigation Institutions,* 247, 257. Duty of water is the area of land upon which a definite volume of water will successfully produce crops. Since different crops need different amounts of water to grow, beneficial use allowed only the maximum volume needed for the specific crop claimed in an application. Virtually every applicant had requested far in excess of his needs.

16. John C. Page, "Memorial to Dr. Elwood Mead," *The Reclamation Era* 11 (November 1936): 249. See: Lawrence B. Lee, "The Canadian-American Irrigation Frontier, 1884–1914," *Agricultural History* 40 (October, 1965): 271–83; and his "American Influences in the Development of Irrigation in British Columbia" in *The Influence of the United States on Canadian Development: Eleven Case Studies* (Durham, N.C.: Duke University Press, 1972): 144–63.

17. Mead, *Irrigation Institutions,* 344–45; Roy M. Robbins, *Our Landed Heritage, The Public Domain, 1776–1936* (Princeton: Princeton University Press, 1942): 326–27.

18. Mead to Charles H. Burritt, January 29, 1892, SECWA; *Annual Report of the Territorial Engineer of Wyoming, 1888* (Cheyenne: Bristol and Knabe Printing Company, 1889), 15–18; *Cheyenne Leader,* December 24, 1893; J. T. Peterson, typescript biography of Elwood Mead, 106–7,

American Heritage Center, University of Wyoming, Laramie (hereafter cited as Peterson Manuscript).

19. Peterson Manuscript, 124; *Cheyenne Leader,* December 24, 1893. Powell's report is a sweeping and perceptive analysis of the problems and the potential of the arid areas of the American West. See: John Wesley Powell, *Report on the Lands of the Arid Regions of the United States* (Washington, D.C.: U.S. Government Printing Office, 1878).

20. *Second Annual Report,* 52–63.

21. *Cheyenne Tribune,* January 10 and 17, 1894.

22. Mead to Francis E. Warren, March 21, 1892, SECWA; Gould, *Wyoming,* 130–32; Anne Carolyn Hansen, "The Congressional Career of Senator Francis E. Warren," *Annals of Wyoming* 20 (January 1948): 39. Information on Smythe and his ideas include Walter Prescott Webb, *The Great Plains* (New York: Ginn and Company, 1931), 357–58; William E. Smythe, *The Conquest of Arid America* (New York: Macmillan Company, 1911); and Lawrence B. Lee, "William E. Smythe and the Irrigation Movement: A Reconsideration," *Pacific Historical Review* 41 (August 1972): 289–311.

23. *Chicago Tribune,* September 1, 1894; Gould, *Wyoming,* 132–33, 202–03.

24. Mead to A. A. Johnson, April 10, 1894, SECWA; [Wyoming Constitutional Convention], file 22–63, ADDI; *Second Biennial Report,* 30; Gould, *Wyoming,* 118–19. Mead's specific objections to the Carey Act included: (1) the delays and expense in procedural matters between Washington and the states; (2) the fact that the costs and responsibility of disposing of the land fell to the state while any profit went to the federal government; (3) no comprehensive plan provided for canal construction; and (4) the absence of any method of uniting grazing and irrigable land. Mead, *Irrigation Institutions,* 26–27.

25. Mead to S. B. Robbins, July 30, 1894; to J. L. VanDerwerker, August 31, 1894; to Fred Bond, September 11, 1894, SECWA; Elwood Mead, *Wyoming as an Agricultural State* (Cheyenne: Tribune Job Printers, 1894), 11–13.

26. Mead to Fred Bond, September 11, 1894; to S. M. Emery, October 12, 1897, SECWA. John T. Ganoe, "The Origins of a National Reclamation Policy," *Mississippi Valley Historical Review* 18 (June 1931): 39. In spite

of these harsh words, Mead continued to correspond with Smythe and their relations seemed friendly. Smythe was laudatory of Mead's work, and when Mead learned of the suspension of *Irrigation Age*, he offered to help wherever possible should Smythe "reopen it." Mead to Smythe, October 16, 1895, SECWA.

27. *Cheyenne Sun-Leader*, February 1, 1896; *New York Journal*, May 23, 1897; *Second Biennial Report*, 30; Larson, *History of Wyoming*, 302–4, 348–51; Charles Lindsay, *The Big Horn Basin* (Lincoln: [University of Nebraska], 1930), 160–234.

28. Mead to Richard J. Hinton, October 9, 1895; to Alva Adams, February 15, 1897, SECWA. *Laramie Republican*, January 29, 1897; *Cheyenne Sun-Leader*, January 26 and 27, 1898; *Second Biennial Report*, 30–32. Elwood Mead, "How Best to Prevent Clashing between Sheep and Cattle Men on the Ranges," *Proceedings of the National Stock Growers Convention* (Denver, Colo., January 25–27, 1898), 94–100.

29. *Chicago Record*, January 26, 1898; *Cheyenne Tribune*, February 26, 1899. Thomas Mead interview, January 3, 1970. Mead told Anson Marston that he had been offered the job of directing irrigation investigations in 1892, but did not feel justified in accepting at that time. About 1895, the irrigation work of the Agriculture Department had been transferred to the Geological Survey. Mead to A. A. Marston, November 22, 1897; to F. H. Newell, February 11, 1898, SECWA.

Chapter 3

1. I am grateful to Doctor Lawrence B. Lee, professor emeritus of San Jose State University, for allowing me to use his unpublished article, "Elwood Mead and the Beginnings of National Reclamation," in writing this chapter. It helped to shape my appreciation and understanding of developments in both California and Washington, D.C., during this period.

2. Peterson manuscript, 262–64; Samuel P. Hays, *Conservation and the Gospel of Efficiency* (Cambridge, Mass.: Harvard University Press, 1959), 243; Donald J. Pisani, *From Family Farm to Agribusiness* (Berkeley: University of California Press, 1984), 342.

3. Unidentified newspaper clippings, T. C. Mead Papers; Peterson Manuscript, 106–7.

4. Unidentified newspaper clippings, T. C. Mead Papers.

5. Mead to Joseph M. Carey, February 15, 1895, SECWA; Adams interview, 98, ROHOUC; Thomas Mead interview, January 3, 1970.

6. Mead to R. B. Howells, November 15, 1895, March 3, 1896; to O. V. P. Stout, March 20, 1896, SECWA.

7. Mead to Newell, February 11, June 20, 1898, SECWA; *Washington Star,* March 13, 1899.

8. Unidentified newspaper clipping, T. C. Mead Papers; Adams interview, 82–83, ROHOUC; Mead, *Irrigation Institutions,* 346; Elwood Mead, "Problems of Irrigation Legislation," *The Forum* 32 (January 1902): 576.

9. Peterson manuscript, 159–70; Mead to Delegates to the National Irrigation Congress, October 15, 1902, Mead Papers, carton 12; Adams interview, 80, ROHOUC; *Great Falls Tribune* (Montana), July 29, 1900; *Denver Republican,* August 20, 1901; Hiram W. Chittenden, "Preliminary Examination of Reservoir Sites in Colorado and Wyoming," *House Document 141,* 55th Cong., 2d sess. (Serial 3666), 6; Ganoe, "Origins of National Reclamation," 40–41; Webb, *Great Plains,* 358–61.

10. Mead to H. G. Burt, n.d., and April 21, 1899, appended to Adams interview, 426–42, ROHOUC.

11. Ibid.

12. Mead to J. S. Dennis, October 20, 1900, carton 12, Mead Papers; George Maxwell to James Wilson, April 29, 1898, file 188-1923, Experiment Stations, General Correspondence, Department of Agriculture [ESGCDA], record group 16, National Archives. *Proceedings of the Ninth Annual Session of the National Irrigation Congress, 1900* (Chicago: n.p., 1901), 270–71; E. Louise Peffer, *The Closing of the Public Domain* (Palo Alto, Calif.: Stanford University Press, 1947), 21.

13. Peffer, *Closing of the Public Domain,* 21–22, 30–32, 38; Gifford Pinchot, *Breaking New Ground* (New York: Harcourt, Brace and Company, 1947), 188–91.

14. Thomas Mead interview, January 3, 1970; Adams interview, 84, 446, ROHOUC; Mead to Benjamin Ide Wheeler, November 12, 1901, University of California Archives, Berkeley [UCAB]; Theodore Roose-

velt, *An Autobiography* (New York: Macmillan Company, 1916), 408–11; Henry F. Pringle, *Theodore Roosevelt, A Biography* (New York: Harcourt, Brace and Company, 1931), 431; Arthur B. Darling, ed., *The Public Papers of Francis G. Newlands,* 2 vols. (New York: Houghton Mifflin Company, 1932), 1:67; Lee, "Elwood Mead." Pinchot claims in his autobiography that he, Newell, Maxwell and W. J. McGee of the Bureau of Ethnology wrote the reclamation part of the message and that Roosevelt "accepted substantially everything we wrote as we wrote it." He quotes part of the message, but omits any passage relative to water laws. *Breaking New Ground,* 188–91. See also M. Nelson McGeary, *Gifford Pinchot* (Princeton: Princeton University Press, 1960), 54.

15. Fred L. Israel, ed., *The State of the Union Messages of the Presidents, 1790–1966,* 2 vols. (New York: Chelsea House-Robert Hector Publishers, 1966), 2:2030–33.

16. Mead to Delegates of National Irrigation Congress, October 15, 1902, Mead Papers, carton 12; William Lilly, III, and Lewis L. Gould, "The Western Irrigation Movement, 1878–1902: A Reappraisal," in *The American West: A Reorientation,* ed. Gene Gressley (Laramie: University of Wyoming Publications, 1966), 72–74.

17. Mead to Wheeler, April 24, 1902, UCAB; Darling, *Public Papers,* I: 68; Roosevelt, *Autobiography,* 411.

18. Mead to Wheeler, February 6, April 24, 1902, UCAB; *Washington Times,* n.d., T. C. Mead Papers; *United States Department of Agriculture Yearbook, 1902,* 735–37. Mead's lack of enthusiasm for the Reclamation Act can also be noted in his final chapter of *Irrigation Institutions,* 344–83.

19. *U.S. Statutes at Large,* 32, 388–90.

20. Ibid.; Alfred R. Golze, *Reclamation in the United States* (New York: McGraw-Hill Book Company, 1952), 102–4; Dorothy Lampen, *Economic and Social Aspects of Federal Reclamation* (Baltimore: Johns Hopkins University Press, 1930), 47–69; James Penick, Jr., *Progressive Politics and Conservation* (Chicago: University of Chicago Press, 1968), 64–65.

21. Adams interview, 425–42, ROHOUC; Hays, *Conservation,* 244.

22. Dunbar, *Forging New Rights,* 134–38. *Kansas v. Colorado* was argued in 1905 but the Supreme Court's decision was not handed down until 1907.

23. Mead to Elon H. Hooker, May 31, 1900, UCAB; Adams interview,

67, ROHOUC. *San Francisco Call,* August 22, 1899; *San Francisco Chronicle,* December 4, 1899; *Los Angeles Times,* April 12, 1899; *United States Department of Agriculture Yearbook* (hereafter cited as *USDA Yearbook*), 1899, 530; *USDA Yearbook,* 1900, 67. Elwood Mead, *Water Rights on the Missouri River and Its Tributaries* (Washington: Government Printing Office, 1899); Mead, *Water Right Problems of the Bighorn Mountains* (Washington: Government Printing Office, 1899); Mead, *The Use of Water in Irrigation* (Washington: Government Printing Office, 1900). Donald J. Pisani, "Water Law Reform in California, 1900–1933," *Agriculture History* 54 (1980): 301–3; and Pisani, *From the Family Farm to Agribusiness,* 335–36.

24. Wheeler to Mead, November 5 and 12, 1900; Mead to Wheeler, November 9, 1900, UCAB. Adams interview, 68, 149–50, ROHOUC.

25. Wheeler to Mead, February 9, 1901; Mead to Wheeler, January 16, 1901, UCAB. Both the Civil Engineering and Agriculture faculties wanted the irrigation studies affiliated with their departments. To avoid conflict, Wheeler set up a separate department, although it became closely aligned with Agriculture because Mead's irrigation investigations cooperated with the Agriculture Experiment Station. Adams interview, 153, 179, ROHOUC.

26. Thomas Mead interview, January 3, 1970; Adams interview, 70, ROHOUC; Mead to Wheeler, June 21, 1901, UCAB; unidentified newspaper clipping, T. C. Mead Papers.

27. Mead to Wheeler, February 6, August 29, September 2 and 23, 1902, January 2, 21, and 27, and June 1, 1903; Wheeler to Mead, September 29, 1902, UCAB. Adams interview, 151, ROHOUC. Mead to George C. Pardee, April 13, 1904; A. C. True to Pardee, November 30, 1904, Pardee Papers, Bancroft Library, University of California.

28. Mead to Wheeler, January 23 and 27, and February 26, 1903; Mead address to California Water and Forest Association, April 22, 1904, UCAB. Mead to E. W. Hilgard, December 20, 1902, Hilgard Papers, Bancroft Library, University of California. *Sacramento Bee,* May 30, 1900; *Record Union* (Sacramento), November 2, 1900. Two unidentified newspaper clippings, T. C. Mead Papers. Mead's annual reports, 1899–1907, in *USDA Yearbooks;* Mead, *Irrigation in Northern Italy,* 2 vols. (Washington: Government Printing Office, 1904–7).

29. Pisani, *From Family Farm to Agribusiness,* 345–51. Maxwell to Wilson, January 13, 1903, file 188-1923, ESGCDA; Mead to Wheeler, February 26 and March 4, 1903. *Redlands Citrograph* (Calif.), January 17 and 24, February 14, and March 4, 1903; *San Francisco Chronicle,* n.d., T. C. Mead Papers. The bill was defeated.

30. Thomas Mead interview, January 3, 1970; Adams, 59, ROHOUC.

31. Wheeler to Mead, May 8, 1906; Mead to Wheeler, May 14, 1906, UCAB.

32. Selar Mead to Mead, January 15, 17, and 26, and February 14, 1891; Daniel B. Mead to Mead February 28, 1891, T. C. Mead Papers. Mead to George Bond, August 12, 1891, SECWA. Mead to E. F. Benson, March 13, 1926; Mead to Reed Smoot, March 18, 1926, file 515, Colonization and Settlement, General Correspondence, Reclamation Bureau [CSGCRB]. Record group 115, National Archives. Mead to L. R. Grimes, December 14, 1922, Mead Papers, carton 1. Mead to Wheeler, April 22, 1903, October 20, 1906, and May 14, 1907, UCAB.

33. Mead to Wheeler, October 20, 1906, and July 16, 1907; Wheeler to Mead, August 5, September 27, 1907, UCAB. Thomas Mead interview, January 3, 1970.

Chapter 4

1. Mead to Wheeler, November 10, 1907, UCAB; I. G. Baker, "Elwood Mead in Australia, An Historical Survey" (typescript), carton 4, Mead Papers 4; author, interview with Lucy Mead Marston, Saratoga, Calif., June 13, 1980.

2. Thomas Mead interview, January 3, 1970. Kylie Tennant, *Australia: Her Story* (London: Macmillan Company, 1962), 201, 237; Marjorie Barnard, *A History of Australia* (New York: Frederick A. Praeger, 1963), 404, 638–39; J. A. LaNauze, *Alfred Deakin,* 2 vols. (Melbourne: Melbourne University Press, 1965), 1:84–88.

3. Tennant, *Australia,* 201–2; LaNauze, *Alfred Deakin,* 1:87–88; Barnard, *History of Australia,* 404–5, 639. Trusts were similar to water districts in the United States.

4. Barnard, *History of Australia,* 294–97; Gordon Greenwood, *Austra-*

lia: A Social and Political History (Sydney: Halstead Press, 1955), 118, 177. Sir Stephen H. Roberts, *History of Australian Land Settlement, 1788–1920* (Melbourne: Macmillan Company of Australia, 1924; repr. 1968), 307–73. Tom Connors, "Closer Settlement Schemes," *The Australian Quarterly* 42, no. 1 (March 1970): 72–75.

5. Roberts, *History,* 350–71; Connors, "Closer Settlement Schemes," 76.

6. Barnard, *History of Australia,* 297, 591; Greenwood, *Australia,* 197, 240; *Yearbook of the Commonwealth of Australia, 1919* (Melbourne: Albert J. Mullett, 1919), 543; Sir Robert Garran, "The Federation Movement and the Founding of the Commonwealth," and W. K. Hancock, "The Commonwealth, 1900–1914," both in J. Holland Rose, et al., eds., *Cambridge History of the British Empire,* 24 vols. (New York: Macmillan Company, 1929–), vol. 7, pt. 1 (Australia), 446–47, 500–503, respectively.

7. Hancock, "Commonwealth," 500–503; Barnard, *History of Australia,* 466–69; *Yearbook of . . . Australia, 1919,* 543; A. G. L. Shaw and H. D. Nicolson, *Australia in the Twentieth Century* (Melbourne: Angus and Robertson, 1967), 56; F. K. Crowley, "1901–1914," in Crowley, ed., *A New History of Australia* (Melbourne: William Heinemann, 1974), 297–300.

8. Baker, "Elwood Mead in Australia"; Mead to Wheeler, February 10, 1908, UCAB; Thomas Mead interview, January 3, 1970.

9. Peterson, "Australian Episode," unpaginated manuscript.

10. Ibid.; Baker, "Elwood Mead in Australia"; A. G. L. Shaw, *A Short History of Australia* (New York: Frederick A. Praeger, 1967), 197, 202–3, 206; Greenwood, *Australia,* 245–48; Barnard, *History of Australia,* 591.

11. Baker, "Elwood Mead in Australia"; Elwood Mead address, "Rural Credits in Australia," n.d., cartons 4 and 12, Mead Papers; Mead, *Report of Investigations of Land Settlement and Irrigation Development in America* (Melbourne: Albert J. Mullett, 1914), 6.

12. Baker, "Elwood Mead in Australia"; Thomas Mead interview, January 3, 1970. Elwood Mead, "Irrigation in Australia," *The Independent* 74 (October 6, 1910), 758–59.

13. Mead to Wheeler, January 16, 1909, UCAB; F. W. Cutlack, "The Murray Waters Question," (Adelaide, 1908). The tone of Mr. Cutlack's remarks can be gleaned from this nine-page pamphlet's subtitle, "Mr.

Elwood Mead and the American Muddle." Baker, "Elwood Mead in Australia."

14. Mead to Tom Mead, January 1, February 10, and March 7, 1909, T. C. Mead Papers; Baker, "Elwood Mead in Australia"; *Yearbook of . . . Australia, 1919,* 265; Mead, "Irrigation in Australia," 758–59.

15. *Yearbook of . . . Australia, 1919,* 265; Mead, "Irrigation in Australia," 761–63.

16. Author, interview with Mrs. George C. Kreutzer, January 7, 1970, Sacramento, Calif.

17. Baker, "Elwood Mead in Australia"; Mead to Wheeler, July 8, 1910, UCAB. *The Argus* (Melbourne), February 2, 11, 12, 19, and 25, March 10, 15, 28, and 31, May 19, June 3 and 24, July 2, August 8, 15, 22, and 31, September 5 and 26, November 2, 3, and 21, 1910.

18. Shaw, *Short History,* 215; *Yearbook of . . . Australia, 1919,* 110; *The Argus,* September 25 and November 28, 1910; Crowley, *New History,* 297–98. From July 1910 to June 1911, 6,008 people arrived under this program, and 40,209 acres were taken up by 757 settlers during this period under the closer settlement program. *State Rivers and Water Supply Commission, Annual Report, 1910–1911* (Melbourne: Albert J. Mullett, 1911).

19. Mead to Tom Mead, March 7 and April 1, 1901, April 5 and 8, May 20, July 23, August 20, and November 29, 1911, T. C. Mead Papers; *The Argus,* September 16, 1909; *Yearbook of . . . Australian 1919,* 265–66.

20. Mead to Tom Mead, October 17 and November 21, 1909, August 25 and September 1, 1910, April 8, May 20, June 4 and 24, and July 23, 1911, T. C. Mead Papers; Mead to Robert E. Jones, March 22, 1923, Mead Papers, carton 3.

21. Mead to Tom Mead, June 24, July 23, October 19, and November 29, 1911, February 10, April 17, and June 12, 1912, T. C. Mead Papers; Mead interview, January 3, 1970.

22. Mead to Lucy Mead, December 15, 1912; Mead to Tom and Lucy Mead, December 25, 1912; Mead to Tom Mead, February 6, 1913, T. C. Mead Papers. Mead to Wheeler, November 11, 1912, and March 10, 1913; Wheeler to Mead, January 25, 1913, UCAB. Thomas Mead interview, January 3, 1970. *The Argus,* July 2 and 26, 1912. Mead also brought back to the United States the body of his close friend, former Wyoming Gov-

ernor William A. Richards, who died of a heart attack in Melbourne on July 25, 1912. Tacetta Walker, "Wyoming's Fourth Governor—William A. Richards," *Annals of Wyoming* 20 (July 1948): 128.

23. Mead to A. C. McClure, December 7, 1922, carton 1, Mead Papers; Greenwood, *Australia*, 240; *The Argus,* October 17, 1912.

24. David J. Gordon, "After Many Years," pamphlet, repr. from *The Advertiser,* August 24, 1915, 1–2; D. I. Wright, "River Murray—A Continuing Debate," *Journal of the Royal Australian Historical Society* 61, no. 3 (September 1975): 165–71; J. H. O. Eaton, *A Short History of the River Murray Works* (Adelaide: K. M. Stephenson, Government Printer, 1945), 7–12.

25. Eaton, *Short History,* 8; Wright, "River Murray," 172; Gordon, "After Many Years," 2.

26. *River Murray Waters Agreement, 1915;* "Memorandum by Mr. Elwood Mead to Victorian Government, 12 April, 1915"; Eaton, *Short History,* 14–16; Gordon, "After Many Years," 3–4; Wright, "River Murray," 174–76; Peterson, "Australian Episode."

27. Mead to Tom Mead, June 6 and 24, September 16, and November 10, 1913; Mead to Tom and Lucy Mead, November 25, 1913; Mr. and Mrs. Alva Adams to Mead, November 7, 1913; Alex B. Cobband to Mead, September 4, 1913, T. C. Mead Papers; Mead to Victor H. Henderson, December 15, 1913, UCAB. *The Age,* August 26, 1913; *The Argus,* August 25, 28, and 29, and September 13, 1913.

28. Mead to Tom Mead, December 12, 1913, T. C. Mead Papers; Adams interview, ROHOUC, 99–101. Wheeler to Mead, January 15, 1914; Mead to Wheeler, March 26, 1914, UCAB. Mead, *Report of Investigations,* 1. *The Argus,* January 1 and 2, March 17, May 29, and June 3 and 4, 1914.

29. Mead to Tom Mead, Easter Sunday [?], July 1, August 24, and September 20, 1914, and January 17, 1915; Mead to Lucy Mead, August 8, 1914, T. C. Mead Papers. Thomas Mead interview, January 3, 1970; Kreutzer interview, January 7, 1970. Eaton, *Short History,* 8; *The Argus,* August 15, 1914.

30. Mead interview, January 3, 1970; Mead to Chester Rowell, January 15, 1915, Chester Rowell Papers, Bancroft Library, University of California; *The Argus,* April 9, 1915.

31. Baker, "Elwood Mead in Australia," S. McTavish to Mead, April 29, 1915; A. E. Lester to Mead, July 4, 1923; C. McDonald to Mead, n.d., carton 4, Mead Papers. *The Argus,* May 1 and 4, 1915.

32. Peterson, "Australian Episode"; *The Argus,* April 14 and 18, June 21 and 27, and August 22, 1914.

33. *The Age,* April 22, 1915, and August 18, 1923. Mead, "What Australia Can Teach America," *The Independent* 71 (August 17, 1911): 370; Conkin, "Vision of Elwood Mead," 89.

Chapter 5

1. Mead to Rowell, November 15, 1914; Rowell to Mead, December 11, 1914, Rowell Papers, Bancroft Library, University of California. Thomas F. Hunt to Mead, April 8, 1915, UCAB; Mead interview, January 3, 1970; Adams interview, 283–85, ROHOUC.

2. Mead to Wheeler, March 9, 1915, UCAB. "Revision of Project Costs," *Reclamation Record* 6 (March 1915): 97–100; Lampen, *Economic and Social Aspects,* 60.

3. Mead to Rowell, June 24, 1915, Rowell Papers, UC; Mead to Wheeler, March 9, 1915, UCAB. Franklin K. Lane to Mead, February 27, 1915; Lane to A. P. Davis, March 11, 1915, file 22-63, ADDI. "Revision of Project Costs," 97–100.

4. "Report of the Central Board of Review on the Carlsbad Project, New Mexico," *Reclamation Record* 7 (July 1916): 298.

5. Ibid, 299–300, 308.

6. Ibid. Central Review Board to Lane, September 27, 1915, carton 18, Mead Papers.

7. *Reclamation Record* 7, 8 (December 1916, January and April 1917); Robbins, *Our Landed Heritage,* 384.

8. Mead to Lane, July 26, 1915, carton 18, Mead Papers.

9. Ibid.

10. Lane to Mead, July 31, 1915, carton 18, Mead Papers.

11. Mead to Lane, July 15, 1915, carton 18, Mead Papers.

12. Mead to Rowell, January 24, 1916, Rowell Papers, UC. Mead,

"Government Aid and Direction in Land Settlement," *American Economic Review,* supplement, 8 (March 1918): 72–75, 82–85.

13. For an excellent discussion of this phenomena, see Peter J. Schmitt, *Back to Nature: The Arcadian Myth in Urban America, 1900–1930* (New York: Oxford University Press, 1969).

14. Mead to Lane, December 17, 1916, file 2-155 (pt. 2), General Land Office, Department of Interior, record group 48, National Archives. *Annual Report of the Department of Labor, 1915,* 43–44; Paul K. Conkin, *Tomorrow a New World* (Ithaca, N.Y.: Cornell University Press, 1959), 49–50.

15. Herbert Hoover to Wheeler, August 13, 1917; Wheeler to Hoover, August 22, 1917, UCAB.

16. R. A. Pearson to W. A. Taylor, May 21 and June 2, 1917; Taylor to Pearson, May 29 and June 2, 1917; H. J. Hough to Mead, May 11, 1917, file R2-7, General Reclamation Projects, Department of Agriculture [GRPDA], record group 48, National Archives.

17. T. Warren Allen to L. W. Page, December 13, 1917; Pearson to [?] Harrison, December 20, 1917; Harrison to Karl Kellerman, December 27, 1917, file R2-7, GRPDA.

18. Mead to G. W. Scott, July 30, 1918, carton 5, Mead Papers; Mead to Lucius E. Pinkham, March 22, 1918, file 8-80, Reclamation Service, Soldier Settlement, Department of Interior [RSSSDI], record group 48, National Archives. For a discussion of the various proposals put forward, see Bill G. Reid, "Proposals for Soldier Settlement during World War I," *Mid-America* 46 (July 1964): 172–86, and Reid, "Franklin K. Lane's Idea for Veterans' Colonization, 1918–1921," *Pacific Historical Review* 33 (November 1964): 447–61; Henry Irving Dodge, "Back to the Land for Soldiers: An Interview with Franklin K. Lane, Secretary of the Interior," *Country Gentleman* 84 (February 15, 1919): 3–4, 43–47; Keith W. Olson, *Biography of a Progressive: Franklin K. Lane, 1864–1920* (Westport, Conn.: Greenwood Press, 1979), 150–52.

19. Lane to Claude Kitchen, September 25, 1919, file 8-80, RSSSDI. "National Soldier Settlement Act," *House Report, 216,* 66th (Cong., 1st sess. (Serial 7592), 12–14. Mead's only objection to the bill was that it required a minimum of five year's residence for title. Mead wanted a ten-

year period in order to prevent speculation. Mead to Lane, October 1, 1919, file 516, CSGCRB.

20. William Cattanach to Mead, October 4, 1918, carton 4, Mead Papers. Mead, *Summary of Soldier Settlements in English-speaking Countries* (Washington, D.C.: Government Printing Office, 1918).

21. Bill G. Reid, "Agrarian Opposition to Franklin K. Lane's Proposal for Soldier Settlement, 1918–1921," *Agricultural History* 41 (April 1967): 168–73. Other proposals for benefits for soldiers included cash bonuses, whose cost varied from 1.2 to 20 billion dollars, depending on the size of the bonus; individual farm loans, which would run from 16 to 40 billion dollars; and loans for city or country homes, estimated at 10 billion dollars. "National Soldier Settlement Act," 2.

22. Lane to Frederick B. Wells, October 20, 1919, file 8-80, RSSSDI; Adams interview, 277–78, ROHOUC. Conkin, *Tomorrow a New World,* 53; Reid, "Agrarian Opposition," 178; and Reid, "Franklin K. Lane's Idea," 459.

23. Mead, *Helping Men Own Farms* (New York: Macmillan Company, 1920); Conkin, *Tomorrow a New World,* 53–54.

Chapter 6

1. Rowell to Mead, December 11, 1914, Rowell Papers; Hunt to Mead, April 8, 1915, UCAB; Thomas Mead interview, January 3, 1970.

2. Rowell to Mead, December 11, 1914, June 30, 1915; Mead to Rowell, March 9, 1916, January 11, 1917; D. N. Morgan to Rowell, May 16, 1917, Rowell Papers. Mead to Tom Mead, February 29, 1916, T. C. Mead Papers; Wheeler to Mead, February 27, 1915, UCAB; Adams interview, 283–85, ROHOUC. Roy J. Smith, "The California State Land Settlements at Durham and Delhi," *Hilgardia* 15, no. 5 (October 1943): 400–401. This article is a one-hundred page analysis of the operations and failure of Durham and Delhi prepared in 1931 for the Giannini Foundation of Agricultural Economics.

3. Cartons 16 and 17 of the Mead Papers are filled with these statements.

4. [Mead], "Protection of Settlers Requires Public Examination and Approval of All Irrigated Colony Enterprises" (typescript of Report of California Commission on Land and Rural Credits, November 29, 1916), carton 16, Mead Papers. Smith, "California State Land Settlements," 401–3.

5. [Mead], "Protection of Settlers." Mead, "Solution of the Land Question," *The New Republic* 6 (April 29, 1916): 348–49.

6. [Mead], "Protection of Settlers."

7. Ibid.; Mead, "State Colonies to be Centers of Purebred Livestock," *The Pacific Rural Press* 94 (September 22, 1917): 277.

8. Mead, *Helping Men Own Farms*, 140–60; Mead, *Government Aid and Direction in Land Settlement* (Fort Collins, Colo.: Courier Press, 1916), 10–11.

9. Harris Weinstock to Hiram V. Johnson, November 10, 1916, carton 16, Mead Papers; Mead to Tom Mead, February 18, 1917, T. C. Mead Papers. Mead to Rowell, January 3, 1917, Rowell Papers. Mead, *Helping Men Own Farms*, 226–27. Smith, "California State Land Settlements," 489; J. T. Peterson, "Durham and Delhi" (manuscript), 7. Of the total funds appropriated, 10,000 dollars was for administrative purposes and 250,000 dollars was to constitute a revolving fund, which was to be repaid to the state within fifty years at 4 percent interest.

10. Smith, "California State Land Settlements," 407–9. Walter E. Packard, "Land and Power Development in California, Greece, and Latin America" (oral history, 1964, Regional Oral History Office, University of California, Berkeley; in the Bancroft Library), 143. Kreutzer interview, January 7, 1970; Kreutzer file, carton 1, Mead Papers. The other members of the Land Settlement Board were Mortimer Fleishhacker, president of the Anglo California Trust Company; ex-senator Frank P. Flint; Prescott F. Cogswell; and Judge William H. Langdon.

11. *California Division of Land Settlement Report, 1927* (Sacramento: State Printing Office, 1928), 3–4, 13; Mead, *Helping Men Own Farms*, 109, 113–22, 174.

12. Mead, *Helping Men Own Farms*, 119–21; *California . . . Land Settlement Report, 1927*, 14.

13. Mead, *Helping Men Own Farms,* 121–24; Packard interview, 152–55, ROHOUC.

14. Mead, *Helping Men Own Farms,* 140–60; Kreutzer interview, January 7, 1970; Smith, "California State Land Settlements," 419. Unfortunately, one load of the cows reacted negatively to the tuberculin test and had to be destroyed. This was in the early days of the settlement and, such was the cooperative spirit at that time, the community contributed voluntarily to absorb half of the cost. Smith, "California State Land Settlements," 419; Mead, *Helping Men Own Farms,* 144.

15. Mead, *Helping Men Own Farms,* 178; Smith, "California State Land Settlements," 410; Packard interview, 152–55, ROHOUC.

16. Mead, *Helping Men Own Farms,* appendix A, 215–28, outlines the differences between the two acts. *California . . . Land Settlement Report, 1927,* 10. Unidentified newspaper clipping, carton 8, Mead Papers; *Stockton California Record,* December 3, 1919; *San Francisco Examiner,* February 20, 1920; *Chico California Enterprise,* March 16, 1920; J. Winter Smith to C. M. Wooster, January 1, 1925, file 8–19, Reclamation Service, Irrigation General, Department of Interior [RSIGDI], record group 48, National Archives. A number of disabled veterans did take up land at Delhi.

17. Smith to Wooster, January 1, 1925, file 8-19, RSIGDI; Adams interview, 288, ROHOUC; Mead to Charles Howard, January 26, 1922, carton 1, Mead Papers. There was considerable controversy over the value of the land at Delhi. One newspaper claimed that Wilson only paid 8 dollars an acre for the land twelve years before he sold it for over 90 dollars. Frank T. Swett, a farmer, said it was worth only $19.53 an acre two years before the board purchased it, while C. M. Wooster placed its value at $30.00 an acre. Frank Adams believed that what Wilson was paid "undoubtedly was too much." On the other hand, Walter Packard doubted that they "could have found a better site under the circumstances." *Merced Sun* (Calif.), February 23, 1923; Wooster to Mark L. Requa, April 6, 1922, carton 2, Mead Papers; Adams interview, 290, and Packard interview, 146–50, ROHOUC; Smith, "California State Land Settlements," 410–17. Frank T. Swett, "California Agricultural Cooperatives" (oral history, 1968, Regional Oral History Office,

University of California, Berkeley; in the Bancroft Library), 52. An ironic twist to the rabbit problem came later as the dying colony conducted periodic "rabbit round-ups" that netted some cash to the residents. They sold the rabbit meat to San Francisco food processors, who used the meat to make chicken tamales! Packard interview, 159–60, ROHOUC.

18. Smith to Wooster, January 1, 1925, file 8-19, RSIGDI. Mead to William H. Brooks, March 21, 1922; "Layout of Plans for Delhi," n.d., carton 1, Mead Papers; Smith, "California State Land Settlements," 411.

19. Mead to E. O. McCormick, December 26, 1922; Mead to Hunt, February 27, 1923; to G. W. Dwinnell, March 24, 1923; Edgar M. Wilson to Mead, April 13, 1922, cartons 1–3, Mead Papers. Packard interview, 150, ROHOUC. Albert Shaw, "California's Farm Colonies," *The American Review of Reviews* 64 (October 1921): 400.

20. Mead to Fremont Older, February 7 and March 11, 1922, carton 1, Mead Papers. *Merced Sun,* February 23, 1923; "Bob" Jones, "Agricultural Leaders of the Pacific West, I—Dr. Elwood Mead," *San Francisco Examiner,* December 10, 1922. For a sample of Mead's contributions, see "Buying a Farm in the New Way: The Success of California's New Plan," *Ladies Home Journal* 36 (June 1919): 36; "Farm Settlements on a New Plan," *The American Review of Reviews* 59 (March 1919), 270–77; "Japanese Land Problem of California," *Annals of the American Academy* 93 (January 1921): 51–55; "New Forty-Niners," *Survey* 47 (January 28, 1922): 651–58; "How to Build Up the Rural West," *Sunset* 50 (June 1923): 32–22. For some articles about Mead and his plan, see W. V. Woehlke, "Be Sure You're Right, Then Stick! How Elwood Mead Rose to the Top on This Principle," *Sunset* 45 (December 1920): 27, and Woehlke, "Food First: How One Western State is Staking the Farmers," *Sunset* 45 (October 1920): 35–38; Vernon L. Cady, "A Western Experiment in Land Settlement," *Survey* 40 (September 21, 1918): 684–86. The *San Francisco Call* ran a series of twenty articles on land settlement in California, and over half of these articles dealt with the "Mead Plan." *San Francisco Call,* January–March 1922.

21. Mead to McCormick, December 29, 1922; Mead to C. L. Seagraves, December 29, 1922; Mead to E. F. Benson, July 28, 1922; Mead to

Willard D. Ellis, February 28, 1923; Mead to William Sproule, March 14, 1923, cartons 1–3, Mead Papers. Packard interview, 197; Swett interview, 52; Adams interview, 290, ROHOUC. Smith to Wooster, January 1, 1925, file 8–19, RSIGDI. There are hundreds of inquiries about land at the two colonies in cartons 1–3, Mead Papers.

22. Mead to Walter Packard, January 19, and February 21 and 28, 1922; Mead to R. I. Rees, July 27, 1922; Mead to Max E. Cook, April 7, 1922; Mead to C. W. Hughett, February 6, 1922; Mead to editor, *Delhi News,* August 7, 1922; Packard to Mead, February 18 and 27, and December 11, 1922, cartons 1–2, Mead Papers. These cartons are filled with requests, many for loans of under one hundred dollars, examined by Mead and many refused as extravagant. The overall picture that emerges is one of a "Big Brother"–type of control over childlike subjects.

23. Smith, "California State Land Settlements," 490–91; Peterson, "Durham and Delhi," 21–22, 47–48; *California . . . Land Settlement Report, 1927,* 5–6.

24. Mead to Alden Anderson, October 20 and November 10, 1922; Mead to Mortimer Fleishhacker, April 10, 1922; Mead to Ben Walker, October 12, 1922; Mead to O. V. P. Stout, May 31, 1922; Mead to Charles F. Neylan, November 13, 1922, cartons 1–2, Mead Papers.

25. Mead to C. C. Davis, March 20, 1922; Mead to Paul Shoup, October 18, 1922; Mead to Alden Anderson, November 10, 1922, cartons 1–2, Mead Papers. "The State Colony Settlements," *Transactions of the Commonwealth Club of California* 16 (November 1921): 276–78.

26. Mead to Stout, May 31, 1922; Mead to A. J. McCune, November 8, 1922; Mead to editor, *San Francisco Call,* n.d.; Mead to Alvin Johnson, January 25, 1923; Mead to Sydney Anderson, December 6, 1922; Mead to R. R. Leslie, December 28, 1922; Mead to Governor William D. Stephens, November 15, 1922, cartons 1–2, Mead Papers. Mead to Tom Mead, November 7 and 17, 1922, T. C. Mead Papers.

27. Mead to Alden Anderson, November 10, 1922, and January 26, 1923; Mead to Edward F. Adams, March 23, 1923; Mead to Guy Earl, February 8, 1923; Mead to Frank English, February 23, 1923, cartons 1 and 3, Mead Papers. Smith to Wooster, January 1, 1925, file 8-19, RSIGDI. *California . . . Land Settlement Report, 1927,* 5.

28. Mead to J. C. Forkner, February 12, 1923, carton 3, Mead Papers; Smith, "California State Land Settlements," 427.

29. Walter V. Woelke, "Food First," 37, 78, 80. Mead to Packard, February 26, 1923; Mead to John H. Finley, November 27, 1922; Mead, "The Meeting of Orientals," cartons 1, 3, 12, Mead Papers. Mead, "Japanese Land Problem," 51–54. A few blacks applied at Delhi, and Mead advised them of a colony in Tulare County, California, where there were all blacks. Mead to O. L. Lyons, January 31, 1923, carton 3, Mead Papers. Kevin Starr, *Inventing the Dream: California through the Progressive Era* (New York: Oxford University Press, 1985), 164–75. Peterson, "Durham and Delhi," 12–13.

30. Mead to A. P. Davis, March 26 and April 3, 1923, file 22–63, ADDI; Smith to Wooster, January 1, 1925, file 8-19, RSIGDI; Gladys Cummings to Mead, June 30, 1923, carton 3. Mead Papers; Adams interview, 289, and Packard interview, 183–92, ROHOUC.

31. Cummings to Mead, June 10, 1923, carton 1, Mead Papers; Mead interview, September 3, 1970; Packard interview, 167, ROHOUC; Smith, "California State Land Settlements," 463–67.

32. Kreutzer interview, January 7, 1970; Thomas Mead interview, January 3, 1970. Adams interview, 291–92, ROHOUC. *California Division of Land Settlement, Final Report, June 30, 1931* (Sacramento: State Printing Office, 1931), 9–15; *California . . . Land Settlement Report, 1927,* 6–13. Sidney T. Harding, "A Life in Western Water Development" (oral history, 1967, Regional Oral History Office, University of California, Berkeley; in the Bancroft Library), 195–97. Smith, "California State Land Settlements," 468, 483–89. Many of Kreutzer's friends believe that his death of a heart attack in 1929 was the result of this ordeal. Kreutzer interview, January 7, 1970.

33. Seagraves to Mead, November 15, 1921; Benson to Mead, December 30, 1921, and November 12, 1922; Mead to Leroy Nickel, January 15, 1923; Mead to Sproule, January 22, 1922, cartons 1–3, Mead Papers. Porter W. Dent to J. B. Lamson, April 18, 1925, file 511, CSGCRB. There is a large folder of unidentified newspaper clippings showing Mead's influence on private colonization schemes in carton 8, Mead Papers.

34. Mead to Benson, February 17, 1927; Mead to Ian Dunlop, November 13, 1926; Mead to Herbert M. Lord, January 21, 1928; Benson to

Mead, March 18, 1926, and February 8, 1927, file 512, CSGCRB. Mead to F. M. Simmons, April 25, 1929, file 146, Administrative Correspondence, Reclamation Bureau [ACRB], record group 115, National Archives. *San Diego Union,* June 17, 1925; *Orland Register* (Calif.), May 29, 1925; Adams interview, 289–93, ROHOUC.

35. Mead to McCormick, December 29, 1922, carton 2, Mead Papers. Packard interview, 147, 197; Adams interview, 293; Harding interview, 202–4, ROHOUC. Smith, "California State Land Settlements," 489–92; Peterson, "Durham and Delhi," 35–39, 43–48. *Washington Post,* March 26, 1929.

Chapter 7

1. Mead to C. T. Johnson, March 19, 1923; Mead to Charles Binder, April 9, 1923, carton 3, Mead Papers.

2. Mead to W. B. Wellman, October 10, 1922; Mead to S. E. H. Soskin, April 3, 1922; Mead to C. C. Davis, March 20, 1922; Mead to Edward F. Adams, March 29, 1923; Mead to G. W. Dwinnell, March 27, 1923; Soskin to Mead, February 23, March 21, 1922, cartons 1–3, Mead Papers. David P. Barrows to Alvey A. Aldee, October 23, 1922, UCAB.

3. "Editorial Comment," *The New Republic* 33 (January 17, 1923): 185. G. W. Dwinnell to Mead, February 9, 1923; Mead to J. C. Forkner, February 12, 1923; Mead to W. H. Code, January 13, 1923; Mead to B. F. Fleming, February 21, 1923; Mead to Frank Freemen, January 13, 1923; Mead to Alvin Johnson, January 25, 1923; Mead to Hiram Johnson, January 2, 1923, carton 1, Mead Papers.

4. *U.S. Statutes at Large,* 42, 108–21. Gavan Daws, *Shoal of Time: A History of the Hawaiian Islands* (New York: Macmillan Company, 1968), 298; Helen Gay Pratt, *Hawaii, Off-Shore Territory* (New York: Charles Scribner's Sons, 1944), 284–85. According to one study, only 2 percent of the land set aside could be developed at a reasonable cost. Lawrence H. Fuchs, *Hawaii Pono: A Social History* (New York: Harcourt, Brace and World, 1961), 174.

5. Mead to Robert Hunter, July 28, 1922; Mead to Ben R. Walker, July 20, 1922; Mead to Alvin Johnson, January 25, 1923; Mead to Albert Shaw,

July 31, 1922; Mead, "Report to Hawaiian Homes Commission" (typescript dated January 12, 1923), 4–6, cartons 1–3, Mead Papers. (New York) *Journal of Commerce*, July 15, 1922; *U.S. Statutes at Large*, 42, 1221–22; Pratt, *Hawaii*, 287–88; Fuchs, *Hawaii Pono*, 258; Daws, *Shoal of Time*, 299.

6. Mead, "Report to Hawaiian Homes Commission," 7–8; George Code to Mead, February 16, 1923, carton 3, Mead Papers. At the end of 1946, more than four thousand Hawaiians were living in various homestead communities. After the original plan failed, a new policy in the 1930s put emphasis on the small residential and subsistence homesteads Mead had recommended. Ralph S. Kuykendall and A. Grove Day, *Hawaii: A History* (New York: Prentice-Hall, 1948), 209. A front page article in the *Wall Street Journal* in September 1991 discussed the Hawaiian Homes Act seventy years after its passage. The authors showed that little has been done in the ensuing years to fulfill the intent of the legislation; only 3,700 families have taken actual possession of homesteads despite tens of thousands of applications. The problems Mead observed and foresaw continue to the present time. *Wall Street Journal*, September 9, 1991, p. 1.

7. Mead to Benson, March 7, 1923; Mead to W. W. Long, March 15, 1923; Mead to Cummings, May 16, 1923; George U. Fuller to Mead, November 20, 1922, carton 3, Mead Papers. Barnard, *History of Australia*, 521–22; Trevor Langford-Smith and John Rutherford, *Water and Land* (Canberra, Australia: Australia National University Press, 1966), 57.

8. Joseph H. Carruthers to Mead, June 13, 15, 1923; Mead to Carruthers, June 14, 1923, carton 4, Mead Papers.

9. Mead to Benson, March 7, 1923; Mead notes on New South Wales (dated June 23, 1923), cartons 3–4, Mead Papers. *Yearbook of the Commonwealth of Australia, 1927* (Melbourne: Albert J. Mullett, 1927), 193. Mr. Justice Pike, *Report on Losses, Soldier Land Settlement* (Canberra: Government Printers, 1929), 6, 9, 23–25.

10. Mead, *Report on the Murrumbidgee Irrigation Scheme* (Sydney: Alfred James Kent, Government Printer, 1923) 3–8; and Mead, *Report on Fodder Conservation* (Sydney: Alfred James Kent, Government Printer, 1923), 4–7. Mead to Hugh McKenzie, July 16, 1923, carton 4, Mead Papers.

{ *Notes to Pages 107–11* 185 }

11. Thomas Mead interview, January 3, 1970. Langford-Smith and Rutherford, *Water and Land,* 57–61, 100–103. The idea of intergrating irrigated and nonirrigated areas was being urged as late as 1966. Ibid., 57.

12. Burns, Philp and Co. to Mead, June 13, 1923, carton 4, Mead Papers.

13. Mead, *Agricultural Development in Palestine* (London: Zionist Executive, August 23, 1924); and Mead, "The New Palestine," *The American Review of Reviews* 70 (December 1924): 623–29.

14. Mead to C. C. Davis, March 20, 1922; Mead to S. E. H. Soskin, February 23, April 3, 1922; Mead to E. F. Adams, March 29, 1923; Soskin to Mead, March 21, 1922, cartons 1–3, Mead Papers.

15. J. Ettingen to Mead, July 15, 1923, carton 3, Mead Papers. Chaim Bermant, *Israel* (New York: Walker and Company, 1967), 7–24; A. Revusky, *Jews in Palestine* (New York: Vanguard Press, 1936), 21–27, 37–50, 125–47. Mead, *Agricultural Development in Palestine,* 6–11.

16. Mead, "New Palestine," 624; and Mead, *Agricultural Development in Palestine,* 6.

17. Mead, *Agricultural Development in Palestine,* 8–11, 15–23.

18. Ibid., 22–23; and Mead, "New Palestine," 623–29. This suggestion seems to foretell accurately the *kibbutz* as a symbol of modern Israel and a major attraction especially for young, idealistic Jews.

19. Adams interview, 351–61, ROHOUC. Mead to Mark Schwartz, director, Palestine Department, Zionist Organization of America, January 27, 1927; Leonard Stein to Mead, September 29, 1927; Leonard Stein to Dr. M. D. Wise, November 3, 1927, Israel Archives, Jerusalem. Mead, et al., "Agricultural Colonization in Palestine" (typescript, December 28, 1927), 3–5, 23, 35, 37, 41, 50, 66.

20. Mead, et al., "Agricultural Colonization in Palestine," 41, 45–46, 48–59, 62–65.

21. Hubert Work to Mead, September 8 and December 14, 1923, carton 3, Mead Papers. *Annual Report of the Commissioner of Reclamation* [ARCR], *1924,* 2–3. Mead told President W. W. Campbell of the university that he would be absent from his teaching duties only in February 1924 when the report was being prepared, and that George Kreutzer would take his classes during that period. Mead to W. W. Campbell, December 28, 1923, carton 3, Mead Papers. The other members of the special

advisers included Thomas E. Campbell, a former governor of Arizona; Dr. John A. Widtsoe, former president of the State University and State Agricultural College of Utah; Oscar E. Bradfute, president of the American Farm Bureau Federation; James R. Garfield, former secretary of the interior; and Clyde C. Dawson, an expert on irrigation law and representative of the U.S. Chamber of Commerce. Press releases, September 10 and 26, 1923, General Records, Committee of Special Advisers on Reclamation, Reclamation Bureau [GRCSARRB], record group 115, National Archives.

22. "Federal Reclamation by Irrigation," *Senate Document 92,* 68th Cong., 1st sess. (Serial 8238), 25–28.

23. Ibid., 1–23; Walter V. Woehlke, "Has Federal Reclamation Failed?" *Sunset* 53 (July 1924): 15. Mead to F. E. Schmitt, December 20, 1923, carton 3, Mead Papers. Mead to James D. Phelan, January 25, 1924, James D. Phelan Papers, Bancroft Library, University of California, Berkeley.

24. Mead, "Special Report to the Special Advisers," n.d., GRCSARRB. "Federal Reclamation by Irrigation," ix.

25. *U.S. Statutes at Large,* 43, 701–4.

26. Mead to W. W. Campbell, March 31, 1924; Fact Finders to Campbell, April 2, 1924, UCAB.

Chapter 8

1. Mead to W. W. Campbell, March 31, 1924, UCAB.

2. Mead to Kreutzer, August 13, 1924; Department of Interior Press Release, August 20, 1924, file 501, CSGCRB.

3. Mead to Edgar M. Wilson, August 28, 1924; to Vera Jane Pease, January 24, 1925, file 503, CSGCBR. Mead to Kreutzer, December 26, 1924, file 301, Construction and Engineering, General, Reclamation Bureau [CEGRB], RG 115, NA.

4. Mead to John A. Widstoe, May 12, 1925, file 301, CEGRB; Work to Calvin Coolidge, July 22, 1925, file 501, CSGCRB. *ARCR, 1925,* 8–11. The moratoriums were on past-due debts for construction and/or operation and maintenance charges. Joint resolutions of Congress provided for delivery of water without reference to delinquency, so that irrigators could receive water even if in arrears on their obligations.

5. *ARCR, 1925,* 4–11. The trend that repayments were taking when Mead assumed office can be seen in the following statistics: From 1920 to 1924, an average of 64.7 percent of construction charges was collected while the 1924 figure was only 46.6 percent. On operation and maintenance charges, an average of 70.2 percent was paid from 1920 to 1924 while the 1924 figure was only 54.4 percent. *ARCR, 1925,* 4–6.

6. *ARCR, 1925,* 4; *ARCR, 1926,* 1; *ARCR, 1929,* 1.

7. Work to Coolidge, July 22, 1925; Kreutzer to J. W. Haw, January 2, 1925, file 501, CSGCRB. Statement by Morrow and Morrow, attorneys for Pathfinder Irrigation District (North Platte, Nebr.), n.d., file 22-63, ADDI. *ARCR, 1925,* 5–6; Kreutzer interview, January 7, 1970; *New York Times,* May 29, 1926.

8. Mead to Widtsoe, May 12, 1925; Mead to F. C. Youngblutt, May 15, 27, 1925; Directors of Belle Fourche Irrigation District to Youngblutt, June 8, 1925, file 301, CEGRB.

9. Golze, *Reclamation,* 244–45; Lampen, *Economic and Social Aspects,* 71–72; *ARCR, 1926,* 2.

10. Mead to H. L. Holgate, February 11, 1926; Press Release, June 11, 1926, file 141.35, Administration Correspondence Reclamation Bureau [ACRB], RG 115, NA. *ARCR, 1926,* 3; "Federal Reclamation by Irrigation," 4–5, 53–58.

11. *ARCR, 1930,* 10–11; "Federal Reclamation by Irrigation," 59–60. Donald Christie Swain, *Federal Conservation Policy, 1921–1933* (Berkeley: University of California Press, 1963), 85.

12. Mead to H. C. Baldridge, November 5, 1928; Mead to Reed Smoot, March 8, 1926, file 501, CSGCRB. "Federal Reclamation by Irrigation," 47; *ARCR, 1924,* 8–24; *ARCR, 1925,* 41–45; *ARCR, 1926,* 27–29, *ARCR, 1929,* 1. Feasibility included such diverse factors as proximity to transportation, crop potentials, and, most importantly, whether construction and operation and maintenance costs could be paid with a profit sufficient to support a farm family.

13. Paul W. Gates, *History of Public Land Law Development* (Washington: Government Printing Office, 1968), 681; Doris Ostrander Dawdy, *Congress in Its Wisdom* (Boulder, Colorado: Westview Press, 1989), 37–41. *New Reclamation Era,* vol. 17 (September, November, 1926, 156, 186; vol. 19 (October, 1928), 151.

14. Mead to Kreutzer, November 20, 1925, file 522, CSGCRB. "Federal Reclamation by Irrigation," 114–16.

15. Mead to Roland P. Hartley, March 10, 1925; Mead to Oro Mc-Dermith, June 1, 1925; Mead to Ray Lyman Wilbur, November 11, 1929, file 522, CSGCRB.

16. Mead to Work, December 17, 1926; Mead to F. A. Kern, February 24 and March 3, 1927; Kern to Mead, February 15 and 24, 1927, May 5 and September 5, 1929; B. E. Stoutemeyer to Mead, March 5, 1927, file 400.08, Lands, General Correspondence, Reclamation Bureau [LGCRB], RG 115, NA. Mead to Kern, November 19, 1928; Mead to Louis C. Cramton, September 9, November 19, 1928; Mead to R. F. Walter, November 15, 1928, file 301, Construction and Engineering, General Correspondence, Reclamation Bureau [CEGCRB], RG 115, NA. Mead to Kern, May 6, October 26, 1929, file 241.31, Finance and Accounts, Reclamation Bureau [FARB], RG 115, NA. Golze, *Reclamation*, 348–49.

17. Mead to W. W. Campbell, January 30, 1925, UCAB; Mead to Tom Mead, January 14, 1925, T. C. Mead Papers.

18. Mead to Kreutzer, November 19, 1924; Mead to R. K. Tiffany, February 4, 1925; Mead to Albert Shaw, March 14, 1925, file 515, SCGCRB.

19. Mead to Richard R. Lyman, March 19, 1926; Mead to John B. Kendrick, March 4, 1926; Mead to R. E. Kelly, June 27, 1927; Mead to W. W. Robertson, July 29, 1926; Mead to Charles B. Stafford, May 19, 1928; Mead to Director, Bureau of the Budget, February 3, 1928; Mead to Coolidge, April 12, 1928; Mead to F. J. Bailey, April 9, 1928; Work to Cramton, March 31, 1926, file 515, CSGCRB.

20. Conkin, *Tomorrow a New World*, 277–80.

21. Mead to delegates to Southern Reclamation Conference, n.d., T. C. Mead Papers. "Reclamation and Rural Development in the South," *House Document 765,* 69th Cong. 2d sess. (Serial 8735), 1–3, 38; "Proceedings of Southern Reclamation Conference," *Senate Document 45,* 70th Cong. 1st sess. (Serial 8870), iv, 1–5, 8–15. *ARCR, 1926,* 2; *The Reclamation Era* 3 (January 1928): 2–3.

22. Mead to Wilbur, May 15, 1929, and January 14, 1932; Mead to Hugh McRae, October 8, 1929, and August 3, 1932; Mead to Alvin Johnson, March 22, 1930; Work to Mead, December 21, 1927; Wilbur to Mead,

May 4, 1929; Wilbur to Addison T. Smith, February 28, 1930; Wilbur to Charles L. McNary, January 7, 1932; Alvin Johnson to Mead, March 26, 1930, file 146, ACRB. *ARCR, 1929,* 6.

23. Mead to Tom Mead, Janaury 14 and 30, February 1 and 23, 1925, and January 1, 1928, T. C. Mead Papers; Mead to W. W. Campbell, January 30, 1925, UCAB; Work to Civil Service Commission, November 16, 1927, file 22-63, ADDI. *ARCR, 1929,* 37.

24. Mead to Tom Mead, January 30, 1925, and January 18, 1927, T. C. Mead Papers; Mead to Alexander Lucas, December 7, 1925, file 515, CSGCRB; Appointment file on Mead, file 22-63, ADDI; Thomas Mead interview, January 3, 1970; Kreutzer interview, January 7, 1970.

25. Appointment file on Mead, file 22-63, ADDI. Mead, "What We Have Done in Haiti," *The New Republic* 48 (November 17, 1926), 378–79. Norris Hundley, Jr., *Dividing the Waters* (Berkeley: University of California Press, 1966), 69–73.

26. Mead to Tom Mead, Janaury 14, 1925, November 19, 1926, January 6, 12, and 22, February 2 and 12, and November 7, 1928, November 20 and December 4, 1929, T. C. Mead Papers; Kreutzer interview, January 7, 1970; J. J. Peterson, Mead Biography, 317. Sue married Edgar F. Kaiser, a son of Henry J. Kaiser, in the early 1930s, and John was married in 1934 after graduating from West Point. Among Kreutzer's survivors was a son, Elwood William, giving some idea of the closeness between the two men.

27. Mead to Cramton, June 17, 1931, file 402, LGCRB; Mead to Wilbur, September 23 and December 21, 1931, file 8-1, Reclamation Service, Organization and Methods, Department of Interior [RSOMDI], RG 48, NA. *ARCR, 1924,* 193; *ARCR, 1930,* 1; *ARCR, 1932,* 1.

28. Mead to Harold L. Ickes, November 6, 1933, file 105.251, ACRB; Mead to Ickes, July 5, 1933, file 402, LGCRB. The income from operation and maintenance charges fell from 1,920,500 dollars in fiscal 1929 to 996,115 dollars in fiscal 1936. The cost of operation and maintenance during the same period was reduced from 1,786,928 dollars in fiscal 1929 to 1,204,053 dollars in fiscal 1936. During those eight years, three years— 1929, 1933, and 1934—showed an excess of receipts over expenditures. *ARCR,* 1929–1932, all p. 1; *Annual Report of the Secretary of the Interior* [*ARSI*], *1933,* 5–6; *1934,* 26–27; *1935,* 49–50; *1936,* 59.

29. *ARCR, 1926,* 6; Peterson, Mead Biography, 337.

30. Mead to Wilbur, January 22, 1933, file 8-1, RSOMDI. *ARCR, 1932,* 6; *ARSI, 1933,* 5.

31. Mead to Ickes, November 6, 1933, file 105.251, ACRB; Appointment file on Mead, files 22-63, 22-64, ADDI; Peterson, Mead biography, 326, 369.

32. Donald C. Swain, "The Bureau of Reclamation and the New Deal, 1933–1940," *Pacific Northwest Quarterly* (July, 1970), 138–44; Gates, *Public Land Law,* 681–83.

33. Mead to Wilbur. n.d., Ray Lyman Wilbur Papers, Herbert Hoover Presidential Library, West Branch, Iowa; Swain, "Bureau of Reclamation", 138; Interview, Mrs. Merril Marston (Mead's daughter, Sue), June 3, 1980, Saratoga, Calif.

34. Gates, *Public Land Law,* 659–60, 685–86.

35. *ARSI, 1934,* 24; Mead, letter to Wilbur, n.d.

36. Mead to Robert G. Sproul, May 14, 1934, UCAB.

37. Porter W. Dent to Ickes, March 19, 1934; Mead to Ickes, April 12, 1934; Ickes to Dent, May 19, 1934, file 8-1, RSOMDI; Peterson, Mead biography, 377; Swain, "Bureau of Reclamation," 142; Thomas Mead interview, January 3, 1970; Marston interview, June 3, 1980.

38. Conkin, *Tomorrow a New World,* 37–38, 87.

39. Ibid., 81, 93–94. Mead to Youngblutt, November 8, 1934, file 510, CSGCRB.

40. Mead to Tom Mead, January 1, 1929, T. C. Mead Papers.

Chapter 9

1. *Boulder Canyon Project: Final Reports, Part 1* (two bulletins, Boulder City, Nevada: Bureau of Reclamation, 1948) [BCPFR, Part 1], Bulletin 1, 116. For a general discussion of the background and building of the Boulder Canyon project, see also Paul L. Kleinsorge, *The Boulder Canyon Project, Historical and Economic Aspects* (Stanford, Calif.: Stanford University Press, 1941); Joseph E. Stevens, *Hoover Dam: An American Adventure* (Norman: University of Oklahoma Press, 1988); Imre Sutton, "Geographical Aspects of Construction Planning: Hoover Dam Revisited,"

Journal of the West 7, no. 3, (July 1968), 301–44. The dam was named for Herbert Hoover by Ray Lyman Wilbur in 1930, but was changed to Boulder Dam by Harold Ickes in 1933. It retained this name until 1946, when it was renamed Hoover Dam. For consistency, I shall refer to it as Boulder Dam throughout.

2. *BCPFR, Part 1*, Bulletin 1, 1–5, 25–27, 33–39, 43.

3. Ibid., 27–28, 33–35; Golze, *Reclamation*, 170.

4. Mead, D. C. Henny, and Joseph Jacobs, "Irrigation and Flood Protection Problems of Imperial Valley, California" (typescript dated March 1917); Mead to Wheeler, November 1, 1916, UCAB.

5. *Annual Report of the Reclamation Service, 1918*, 381–82; ibid., *1920*, 417, 476–77; *BCPFR, Part 1*, Bulletin 1, 44; Elwood Mead, W. W. Schlecht, and C. E. Grunsky, *The All-American Canal, Report of the All-American Canal Board* (Washington: Government Printing Office, 1920), 63–64; Hundley, *Dividing the Waters*, 46–48; "Problems of Imperial Valley and Vicinity," *Senate Document 142*, 67th Cong., 2d sess. (Serial 7977), 85.

6. "Problems of Imperial Valley," 21.

7. "The Hoover Dam Documents," *House Document 717*, 80th Cong., 2d sess. (Serial 11229), Appendix 203; Hundley, *Dividing the Waters*, 51. For an excellent discussion of the developments concerning the Colorado River Compact, see Norris Hundley, Jr., *Water and the West: The Colorado River Compact and the Politics of Water in the American West* (Berkeley: University of California Press, 1975).

8. "Hoover Dam Documents," 38–43; *BCPFR, Part 1*, Bulletin 1, 52. For a general discussion of this struggle, see Beverley Bowen Moeller, *Phil Swing and Boulder Dam* (Berkeley: University of California Press, 1971).

9. Mead to Hiram Johnson, January 19, 1926; Johnson to Mead, January 20, 1926, file 522, Colorado River–Imperial Valley Project, Reclamation Bureau [CRIVPRB], record group 115, National Archives. *BCPFR, Part 1*, Bulletin 1, 53; John D. Hicks, *Republican Ascendency, 1921–1933* (New York: Harper and Row, 1960), 125; Swain, *Federal Conservation Policy*, 90.

10. *U.S. Statutes at Large*, 45, 1057–66.

11. Mead to Grace Raymond Hebard, n.d., Hebard Collection; Mead to Wilbur, January 10 and May 15, 1930, Ray Lyman Wilbur Papers, Her-

bert Hoover Presidential Library, West Branch, Iowa. *BCPFR, Part 1,* Bulletin 2, 17, 291–356. The contracts allotted 36 percent of the firm power to the Metropolitan Water District of Southern California; 13 percent to the City of Los Angeles; 9 percent to Southern California Edison Company; 6 percent to smaller California municipalities; and 18 percent each to Arizona and Nevada. Mead to Wilbur, May 15, 1930, Wilbur Papers.

12. "International Water Commission, United States and Mexico," *House Document 359,* 71st Cong. 2d sess. (Serial 9233), 27–28, 488–91; Hundley, *Dividing the Waters,* 57–58, 67–68. Mead to Wilbur, April 10, 1929, Foreign Affairs, Presidential Papers [FAPP], Herbert Hoover Presidential Library, West Branch, Iowa.

13. "International Water Commission," 14–75; Hundley, *Dividing the Waters,* 68–74. Mead statement attached to letter, Wilbur to Hoover, November 5, 1929, FAPP. In the letter, Wilbur told the president, "it seems to me that there will be no settlement of this question [Mexico's share of the water] unless we purchase lower California." An agreement was finally reached in 1944.

14. *BCPFR, Part 1,* Bulletin 1, 53, 72–73; Bulletin 2, 11. *The Reclamation Era* 3 (September 1928): 133.

15. Wilbur to Mead, July 4, 1930, file 8-3, pt. 2, Colorado River Storage Administration, Department of Interior [CRSADI], record group 48, National Archives. *BCPFR, Part 1,* Bulletin 1, 84–85; *ARCR, 1929,* 2; *ARCR, 1930,* 2–3. Mead, "Conquering the Colorado," *The American Review of Reviews* 80 (September 1929): 55, 58–60.

16. J. Mason Rupert to Willa Klug Baum, April 1958, 314, ROHOUC; Mead interview, January 3, 1970. Mead to Lynn Atkinson, January 6, 1930, file 214, CRIVPRB; Harry E. Crain to Ickes, February 15, 1936, file 22-63, ADDI. *ARCR, 1930,* 3–4.

17. Mead to Wilbur, April 26, 1930; press release, Department of Interior, July 29, 1929; Porter W. Dent memo, January 31, 1931, file 402, CRIVPRB. Mead to Oswald Garrison Villard, October 20, 1931, file 107, CRIVPRB. Ray Lyman Wilbur, Jr., "Boulder City: A Survey of Its Legal Background, Its City Plan and Its Administration" (Master's thesis, Syracuse University, 1935), 116. Mead was conscious that Congress was keeping a close watch on extravagance in the building program for Boul-

der City. For example, he suggested to Raymond F. Walter, chief engineer for the project, that the term *club house* be dropped in favor of *dormitory,* to "safeguard" against congressmen who were "pretty finicky" about the expenses of Boulder City. Mead to R. F. Walter, March 17, 1931, file 412, CRIVPRB.

18. Mead, notes on his meeting with Governor Fred B. Balzer of Nevada, February 6, 1932; Mead to W. A. Bechtel of Six Companies, March 21, 1933; Mead to Wilbur, January 3, 1931; Mead to Thelen and Marrin, attorneys, June 17, 1931, file 402, CRIVPRB. Wilbur to Balzer, June 3, 1932; Wilbur to Secretary of Labor, January 29, 1932; Mead to Ickes, March 27, 1934; S. R. Whitehead to Wilbur, December 30, 1930, file 8-3, CRSADI. Wilbur, "Boulder City," 120, 145; *The Reclamation Era* 22 (February 1931): 28.

19. Cramton to Mead, June 29 and October 1, 1931; Dent to Mead, July 1, 1931; Mead to Walker R. Young, October 3 and 26, 1931; Mead to Ickes, March 31, 1934; Young to Mead, October 20 and December 31, 1931, and September 13, 1932; Young to Walter, January 4, 1932, file 402, CRIVPRB. Mead to Young, August 31, 1932; Mead press release, August 28, 1932; Sims Ely to Ted Burns, October 22, 1932, file 107, CRIVPRB. Wilbur to Phil D. Swing, June 2, 1932; Wilbur to Senator David I. Walsh, December 7, 1932; Wilbur to Six Companies, May 15, 1933; Boulder City Chamber of Commerce to Ickes, March 28, 1934, file 8-3, pts. 2–3, CRSADI.

20. Wilbur to William L. Sibert, December 5, 1930, file 8-3, CRSADI; Mead to Atkinson, October 30, 1930, file 214, CRIVPRB. *BCPFR, Part I,* Bulletin 1, 88; Wilbur, "Boulder City," 76.

21. Mead to Wilbur, October 8, 1929, file 214, CRIVPRB; Wilbur to Secretary of Labor, January 29, 1932, file 8-3, pt. 2, CRSADI. *BCPFR, Part I,* Bulletin 1, 85–89.

22. *BCPFR, Part I,* Bulletin 1, 83, 88.

23. Mead to Villard, August 24 and October 20, 1931; Mead to Swing, November 25, 1931; Swing to Mead, November 21, 1931, file 107, CRIVPBR. Mead to Editor, *Omaha World-Herald,* June 29, 1932, file 8-3 CRSADI. *Los Angeles Times,* August 27, 1931; *The New Republic* 67 (August 26, 1931): 48. Worth M. Tippy, "The Situation at Hoover Dam" (typescript report, September 7, 1931), Colorado River, Presidential Papers [CRPP], Her-

bert Hoover Presidential Library, West Branch, Iowa. *BCPFR, Part 1,* Bulletin 1, 89. Edmund Wilson, "Hoover Dam," *The New Republic* 68 (September 2, 1931): 66–69.

24. Mead to Villard, August 24 and October 20, 1931; Young to General Strike Committee, August 11, 1931, files 107, 107.2, CRIVPBR. Tippy, "Situation at Hoover Dam," CRPP. *Los Angeles Times,* August 27, 1931; Wilson, "Hoover Dam," 66–69; Mead, "Boulder Dam" (Letter to editor), *New Republic,* August 26, 1931, 48. Mead to editor, *Omaha World-Herald,* June 29, 1932, file 8-3, CRSADI.

25. Letters to Wilbur from William H. King, March 10, 1932; from Henry F. Ashurst, March 23 and April 6, 1932; from Carl Hayden, March 24, 1932; from John N. Garner, March 28, 1932; from National Association for the Advancement of Colored People, May 4, 1932; from M. A. Bechtel, June 22 and July 11, 1932; Wilbur to Ashurst, April 12, 1932; Wilbur to Walter White, June 10, 1932; White to Harry Slattery, assistant to Ickes, April 9, 1934; Slattery to White, April 24, 1934, file 8-3, CRSADI. Mead to Wilbur, June 15, 1932; Mead to James E. Watson, July 28, 1932; Mead to Ickes, October 11, 1932; Mead to Young, October 16, 1933; Mead to Robert C. Weaver, November 9, 1934, file 107.5, CRIVPRB.

26. Wilbur to Jesse H. Metcalf, May 3, 1932, file 8-3, CRSADI; Mead to Key Pittman, June 6, 1932; Mead to Hiram Johnson, June 6, 1932, file 241.33, CRIVPRB; Mead to Walker R. Young, May 27, August 31, 1932, file 107, CRIVPRB. Wilbur to Hoover, with attached memo, Mead to Wilbur, May 24, 1932, CRPP. Kleinsorge, *Boulder Canyon Project,* 212.

27. See Stevens, *Hoover Dam,* for the drama and detail of actual construction.

28. Mead to Scott Leavitt, May 25, 1932, file 402, CRIVPRB; Mead to Walter, June 1, 1933; Mead to F. Schnepfe, June 21, 1933, file 246, CRIVPRB; Mead to George Soule, September 28, 1933; Northcutt Ely to assistant secretary of the interior, September 7, 1932, file 107, CRIVPRB. Mead to *Omaha World-Herald,* June 29, 1932; Mead to Walter, September 7, 1932; Mead to Ickes, March 1, 1935; Dunbar G. Burdick, confidential report to Ickes, April 30, 1934, file 8-3, CRSADI.

29. F. T. Crowe to Mead, February 28, 1935; Mead to Ickes, March 1, 1935; Ickes to Mead, March 4, 1935; Ickes to Henry J. Kaiser, March 5, 15, and 29, and July 13, 1935; Kaiser to Ickes, March 4, June 27, 1935; Ickes to

Key Pittman, March 15, 1935; Slattery to Ickes, March 6, 1935; Paul A. Marrin to Ickes, August 12, 1935; Frank T. Wright to Ickes, February 4, 1936; John C. Page, acting commissioner, to Burlew, April 6, 1936, file 8-3 CRSADI. Memo, Young to Those in Charge of Engineering and Inspection, March 15, 1935; Kaiser to Ickes, July 26, 1935; Ickes to Glavis, November 14, 1935, file 107.1, CRIVPRB. This was hardly an excessive fine since the Six Companies reportedly made eighteen million dollars on the forty-eight million dollar contract.

30. Mead to Ickes, July 18 and 27, and August 5, 1935; Ickes to Mead, September 3, 1935, file 107.2, CRIVPRB. Ickes to William Green, December 21, 1934, file 8-3, CRSADI.

31. Mead to E. K. Burlew, December 11, 1934; Burlew to E. W. Clark, December 20, 1934, file 8-3, CRSADI. The construction of Grand Coulee Dam was begun in 1933, but the bulk of the work was done after Mead's death. Although he had long advocated the project, Mead had little to do with its construction. His "monument" was the Colorado River project. Mead to A. P. Davis, January 29, 1923, Mead Papers, box 3, Berkeley. Golze, *Reclamation,* 176–78; Swain, *Federal Conservation Policy,* 91–93; "They Stand Out from the Crowd," *The Literary Digest* 116 (September 23, 1933): 9.

32. Mead to Ickes, May 24 and December 27, 1933; Mead to Colonel Waite, December 6, 1933; Mead to Walter, December 11, 1933, file 246, CRIVPRB. *BCPFR, Part 1,* Bulletin 1, 123–28.

33. Monthly report of persons employed by the contractors of Boulder Dam, file 107.01, CRIVPRB; unidentified newspaper clipping, Hebard Collection. Kleinsorge, *Boulder Canyon Project,* 213. Peterson biography, 400.

34. Press release, Department of the Interior, February 14, 1936, file 22-63, ADDI. Tom Mead interview, January 3, 1970.

Selected Bibliography

Primary Material

Manuscripts, Personal

Heberd, Grace Raymond. Papers. Heberd Collection, Western History Research Center, University of Wyoming, Laramie.

Hilgard, Eugene W. Papers. Bancroft Library, University of California.

Hoover, Herbert. Papers. Herbert Hoover Presidential Library, West Branch, Iowa.

Mead, Elwood. Papers and Correspondence, 22 cartons. Bancroft Library, University of California.

Mead, Thomas Chase. Personal Papers of Elwood Mead in (son) T. C. Mead's possession. Boulder City, Nevada.

Pardee, George C. Papers. Bancroft Library, University of California.

Phelan, James D. Papers. Bancroft Library, University of California.

Rowell, Chester H. Papers. Bancroft Library, University of California.

University of California Archives, Berkeley, 1900–1936.

Wilbur, Ray Lyman. Papers. Herbert Hoover Presidential Library, West Branch, Iowa.

Official Government Records
ISRAEL

Records Relating to Colonization in Palestine in 1920s. Israel Archives, Jerusalem.

UNITED STATES

Bureau of Agricultural Engineering Records, Irrigation Investigations
Division. Record Group 8, National Archives.
Department of Agriculture. Record Group 16, National Archives.
Department of Interior. Record Group 48, National Archives.
Reclamation Bureau. Record Group 115, National Archives.

WYOMING

Letterpress Books of the Governors, 1869–1907. Wyoming State Archives and Historical Department, Cheyenne.
State Engineer's Office. Cheyenne.
State Engineer's Correspondence, 1891–1898. Wyoming State Archives
and Historical Department, Cheyenne.

Official Government Publications
AUSTRALIA

Mead, Elwood. *Report of Investigations of Land Settlement and Irrigation
Development in America*. Melbourne: Albert J. Mullett, 1914.
———. *Report on Fodder Conservation*. Sydney: Alfred James Kent, Gov-
ernment Printer, 1923.
———. *Report on the Murrumbidgee Irrigation Scheme*. Sydney: Alfred
James Kent, Government Printer, 1923.
———. *River Murray Waters Agreement, 1915*. Memorandum by Elwood
Mead to Victorian Government, April 12, 1915.
Pike, Mr. Justice. *Report on Losses, Soldier Land Settlement*. Canberra: Gov-
ernment Printers, 1929.
Yearbook of the Commonwealth of Australia, 1919. Melbourne: Albert J. Mul-
lett, 1919.
Yearbook of the Commonwealth of Australia, 1927. Melbourne: Albert J. Mul-
lett, 1927.

CALIFORNIA

California Division of Land Settlement Reports, 1918–1930. Sacramento: State Printing Office, 1918–1930.
California Division of Land Settlement, Final Report, June 30, 1931. Sacramento: State Printing Office, 1931.

COLORADO

Second Biennial Report of the State Engineer of the State of Colorado, 1883–1884. Denver: Collier and Cleaveland Lith. Co., 1887.
Third Biennial Report of the State Engineer of the State of Colorado, 1885–1886. Denver: Collier and Cleaveland Lith. Co., 1887.

ISRAEL

Mead, Elwood. *Agricultural Development in Palestine.* London: Zionist Executive, 1924.

UNITED STATES

Annual Report of the Commissioner of Reclamation, 1924–1932.
Annual Report of the Department of Labor, 1915.
Annual Report of the Reclamation Service, 1918–1923.
Annual Report of the Secretary of the Interior, 1933–1936.
Boulder Canyon Project: Final Reports, Part 1. 2 bulletins. Boulder City, Nevada: Bureau of Reclamation, 1948.
Chittenden, Hiram W. "Preliminary Examinations of Reservoir Sites in Colorado and Wyoming," *House Document 141.* 55th Cong., 2d sess. Serial 3666.
"Federal Reclamation by Irrigation," *Senate Document 92.* 68th Cong., 1st sess. Serial 8238.
"The Hoover Dam Documents," *House Document 717.* 80th Cong., 2d sess. Serial 11229.
"International Water Commission, United States and Mexico," *House Document 359.* 71st Cong., 2d sess. Serial 9233.

Mead, Elwood, W. W. Schlecht, and C. E. Grunsky. *The All-American Canal, Report of the All-American Canal Board*. Washington: Government Printing Office, 1920.

Mead, Elwood. *Irrigation in Northern Italy*. 2 vols. Washington: Government Printing Office, 1904–7.

―――. *Summary of Soldier Settlements in English-speaking Countries*. Washington: Government Printing Office, 1918.

―――. *The Use of Water in Irrigation*. Washington: Government Printing Office, 1900.

―――. *Water Right Problems of the Bighorn Mountains*. Washington: Government Printing Office, 1899.

―――. *Water Rights on the Missouri and Its Tributaries*. Washington: Government Printing Office, 1899.

"National Soldier Settlement Act," *House Report 216*. 66th Cong., 1st sess. Serial 7592.

Powell, John Wesley. *Report on the Lands of the Arid Regions of the United States*. Washington: Government Printing Office, 1878.

"Problems of Imperial Valley and Vicinity," *Senate Document 142*. 67th Cong., 2d sess. Serial 7977.

"Proceedings of Southern Reclamation Conference," *Senate Document 45*. 70th Cong., 1st sess. Serial 8870.

"Reclamation and Rural Development in the South," *House Document 765*. 69th Cong., 2d sess. Serial 8735.

United States Department of Agriculture Yearbook. 1899–1907.

U.S. Statutes at Large, 32.

U.S. Statutes at Large, 42.

U.S. Statutes at Large, 43.

U.S. Statutes at Large, 45.

VICTORIA

State Rivers and Water Supply Commission, Annual Report. 1908–15.

WYOMING

Journals and Debates of the Constitutional Convention of the State of Wyoming. Cheyenne: The Daily Sun, 1893.

Second Annual Report of the Territorial Engineer of Wyoming, 1889. Cheyenne: Bristol and Knabe Printing Company, 1890.
Second Biennial Report of the State Engineer of Wyoming, 1893–1894. Cheyenne: Bristol and Knabe Printing Company, 1895.

Newspapers and Periodicals

Cheyenne Leader, 1893.
Cheyenne Sun-Leader, 1896–98.
Cheyenne Tribune, 1894–99.
Chicago Record, 1898.
Chicago Tribune, 1894.
Chico California Enterprise, 1920.
Denver Republican, 1910.
Great Falls Tribune (Montana), 1900.
Laramie Republican, 1897.
Los Angeles Times, 1899.
(Melbourne) *The Age*, 1915, 1923.
(Melbourne) *The Argus*, 1909–1916.
Merced Sun (California), 1923.
New York Journal, 1897.
(New York) *Journal of Commerce*, 1922.
New York Times, 1919–1936.
Orland Register (California), 1925.
Reclamation Record, 1915–1924.
The Reclamation Era, 1924–1936.
Redlands Citrograph (California), 1903.
Sacramento Bee, 1900.
(Sacramento) *Record Union*, 1902.
San Diego Union, 1925.
San Francisco Call, 1899, 1922.
San Francisco Chronicle, 1899.
San Francisco Examiner, 1920.
Stockton California Record, 1919.
Washington Post, 1929.
Washington Star, 1899.

Interviews

Adams, Frank. Interview by Willa Klug Baum, Winter and Spring 1958. Typescript, Regional Oral History Office, University of California, Berkeley.

Harding, Sidney T. "A Life in Western Water Development." Oral history, 1967, Regional Oral History Office, University of California, Berkeley.

Kreutzer, Mrs. George C. Interview with author, January 7, 1970, Sacramento, California.

Marston, Lucy Mead. Interview with author, Saratoga, California, June 13, 1980.

Mason, J. Rupert. Interview by Willa Klug Baum, April 1958. Typescript, Regional Oral History Office, University of California, Berkeley.

Mead, Thomas Chase. Interview with author, January 3, 1970, Boulder City, Nevada.

Packard, Walter E. Interview by Willa Klug Baum, April 1964. Typescript, Regional Oral History Office, University of California, Berkeley.

Swett, Frank T. Interview by Willa Klug Baum, May 1961. Typescript, Regional Oral History Office, University of California.

Books and Pamphlets

Cutlack, F. W. "The Murray Waters Question. Mr. Elwood Mead and the American Muddle." Pamphlet. Adelaide, n.p., 1908.

Gordon, David J. "After Many Years." Pamphlet, repr. from *The Advertiser* (Melbourne), August 24, 1915.

Mead, Elwood. *Agricultural Development in Palestine*. London: Zionist Executive, 1924.

———. *Government Aid and Direction in Land Settlement*. Fort Collins, Colo.: The Courier Press, 1916.

———. *Helping Men Own Farms*. New York: Macmillan Company, 1920.

———. *Irrigation Institutions*. New York: Macmillan Company, 1903.

———. *The Ownership of Water*. Denver: Times Printing Works, 1887.

———. *Wyoming as an Agricultural State*. Cheyenne: Tribune Job Print-
ers, 1894.
Roosevelt, Theodore. *An Autobiography*. New York: Macmillan Com-
pany, 1916.
Smythe, William E. *The Conquest of Arid America*. New York: Macmillan
Company, 1911.

Articles

Cady, Vernon M. "A Western Experiment in Land Settlement." *Survey*
40 (September 21, 1918): 684–86.
Dodge, Henry Irving. "Back to the Land for Soldiers: An Interview with
Franklin K. Lane, Secretary of the Interior." *Country Gentleman* 84
(February 15, 1919): 3–4, 43–47.
"Editorial Comment." *The New Republic* 33 (January 17, 1923): 185.
Jones, "Bob." "Agricultural Leaders of the Pacific West, I—Dr. Elwood
Mead." *San Francisco Examiner,* December 10, 1922.
Mead, Elwood. "Buying a Farm in the New Way: The Success of Cali-
fornia's New Plan." *Ladies Home Journal* 36 (June 1919): 36.
———. "Community Farming." *The New Republic* 41 (February 18, 1925):
327–32.
———. "Conquering the Colorado." *The American Review of Reviews* 80
(September 1929): 54–60.
———. "Farm Settlements on a New Plan." *The American Review of Re-
views* 59 (March 1919): 270–77.
———. "Government Aid and Direction in Land Settlement." *American
Economic Review,* Supplement, 8 (March 1918): 72–98.
———. "How Best to Prevent Clashing between Sheep and Cattle Men
on the Ranges." *Proceedings of the National Stock Growers Convention*
(Denver), January 25–27, 1898, 94–100.
———. "How to Build Up the Rural West." *Sunset* 50 (June 1923): 32–33.
———. "Irrigation in Australia." *The Independent,* 74 (October 6, 1910):
756–63.
———. "Japanese Land Problem of California." *Annals of the American
Academy* 93 (January 1921): 51–55.

———. "New Forty-niners." *Survey* 47 (January 28, 1922): 651–58.

———. "The New Palestine." *The American Review of Reviews* 70 (December 1924): 623–29.

———. "Problems of Irrigation Legislation." *The Forum* 32 (January 1902): 573–81.

———. "Rural Life in America." *The American Review of Reviews* 73 (March 1926): 303–4.

———. "Solution of the Land Question." *The New Republic* 6 (April 29, 1916): 348–49.

———. "State Colonies to be Centers of Purebred Livestock." *The Pacific Rural Press* 94 (September 22, 1917): 277.

———. "What Australia Can Teach America." *The Independent* 71 (August 17, 1911): 367–71.

———. "What We Have Done In Haiti." *The New Republic,* 48 (November 17, 1926): 378–79.

"Report of the Central Board of Review on the Carlsbad Project, New Mexico." *Reclamation Record* 7 (July 1916): 298–308.

"Revision of Cost Projects." *Reclamation Record* 6 (March 1915): 97–100.

Shaw, Albert. "California's Farm Colonies." *The American Review of Reviews* 64 (October 1921): 397–404.

"The State Colony Settlements." *Transactions of the Commonwealth Club of California* 16 (November 1921): 260–85.

"They Stand Out From the Crowd." *The Literary Digest* 116 (September 23, 1933): 9.

Wilson, Edmund. "Hoover Dam." *The New Republic* 68 (September 2, 1931): 66–69.

Woehlke, W. V. "Be Sure You're Right, Then Stick! How Elwood Mead Rose to the Top on This Principle." *Sunset* 45 (December 1920): 27.

———. "Has Federal Reclamation Failed?" *Sunset* 53 (July 1924): 14–15.

———. "Food First: How One Western State Is Staking the Farmers." *Sunset,* 45 (October 1920): 35–38.

Miscellaneous Material

Eighth Census of the United States, 1860. National Archives.

Mead, Elwood. "Agricultural Colonization in Palestine. Typescript, December 28, 1927, 84 pp. Israel Archives, Jerusalem.

———. "Tobacco." Handwritten Thesis in Agriculture, Purdue University, Thesis no. 30, 1882.
Proceedings of the Ninth Annual Session of the National Irrigation Congress, 1900. Chicago: n.p., 1901.

Secondary Works

Bibliographies

Dodds, Gordon B. "Conservation and Reclamation in the Trans-Mississippi West: A Critical Bibliography." *Arizona and the West* 13, no. 2 (Summer 1971): 143–71.
Lee, Lawrence B. *Reclaiming the American West.* Santa Barbara: ABC-Clio Press, 1980.

Books

Barnard, Marjorie. *A History of Australia.* New York: Frederick A. Praeger, 1963.
Bermant, Chaim. *Israel.* New York: Walker and Company, 1967.
Boyd, David. *Greeley and the Union Colony.* Greeley, Colo.: Greeley Tribune Press, 1890.
Conkin, Paul K. *Tomorrow a New World.* Ithaca, N.Y.: Cornell University Press, 1959.
Crowley, F. K., ed. *A New History of Australia.* Melbourne: William Heineman, 1974.
Darling, Arthur B., ed. *The Public Papers of Francis G. Newlands,* 2 vols. New York: Houghton Mifflin Company, 1932.
Dawdy, Doris Ostrander. *Congress in Its Wisdom: The Bureau of Reclamation and the Public Interest.* Boulder, Colorado: Westview Press, 1989.
Daws, Gavan. *Shoal of Time: A History of the Hawaiian Islands.* New York: Macmillan Company, 1968.
Dufour, Perret. *The Swiss Settlement of Switzerland County, Indiana.* Indianapolis: Indiana Historical Commission, 1925.

Dunbar, Robert G. *Forging New Rights in Western Waters*. Lincoln: University of Nebraska Press, 1983.

Eaton, J. H. O. *A Short History of the River Murray Works*. K. M. Stephenson, Government Printer, Adelaide, 1945.

Fuchs, Lawrence H. *Hawaii Pono: A Social History*. New York: Harcourt, Brace and World, 1961.

Gates, Paul W. *History of Public Land Law Development*. Washington, D.C.: U.S. Government Printing Office, 1968.

Garran, Sir Robert. "The Federation Movement and the Founding of the Commonwealth," in vol. 7, pt. 1, *Cambridge History of the British Empire,* ed. J. Holland Rose et al. 24 vols. New York: Macmillan Company, 1929–.

Golze, Alfred R. *Reclamation in the United States*. New York: McGraw-Hill Book Company, 1952.

Gould, Lewis L. *Wyoming, A Political History, 1868–1896*. New Haven: Yale University Press, 1968.

———. *History of Wyoming*. Lincoln: University of Nebraska Press, 1978.

Greenwood, Gordon. *Australia: A Social and Political History*. Sydney: Halstead Press, 1955.

Hancock, W. K. "The Commonwealth, 1900–1914," in vol. 7, pt. 1, *Cambridge History of the British Empire,* ed. J. Holland Rose et al. 24 vols. New York: Macmillan Company, 1929–.

Hays, Samuel P. *Conservation and the Gospel of Efficiency*. Cambridge: Harvard University Press, 1959.

Hepburn, William. *Purdue University: Fifty Years of Progress*. Lafayette, Ind.: Purdue University Press, 1924.

Hicks, John D. *Republican Ascendency, 1921–1933*. New York: Harper and Row, 1960.

Hundley, Norris, Jr. *Dividing the Water*. Berkeley: University of California Press, 1966.

———. *Water and the West: The Colorado River Compact and the Politics of Water in the American West*. Berkeley: University of California Press, 1975.

Israel, Fred L., ed. *The State of the Union Messages of the Presidents, 1790–1966*. 3 vols. New York: Chelsea House-Robert Hector Publishers, 1966.

Kleinsorge, Paul L. *The Boulder Canyon Project, Historical and Economic Aspects*. Stanford, Calif.: Stanford University Press, 1941.

Kuykendall, Ralph S., and A. Grove Day. *Hawaii: A History*. New York: Prentice-Hall, 1948.

Lampen, Dorothy. *Economic and Social Aspects of Federal Reclamation*. Baltimore: Johns Hopkins University Press, 1930.

Langford-Smith, Trevor, and John Rutherford. *Water and Land*. Canberra: Australia National University Press, 1966.

LaNauze, J. A. *Alfred Deakin*. 2 vols. Melbourne: Melbourne University Press, 1965.

Larson, Taft A. *History of Wyoming*. Lincoln: University of Nebraska Press, 1965.

Lindsay, Charles. *The Big Horn Basin*. Lincoln: [University of Nebraska], 1930.

McGeary, M. Nelson. *Gifford Pinchot*. Princeton: Princeton University Press, 1960.

Moeller, Beverley Bowen. *Phil Swing and Boulder Dam*. Berkeley: University of California Press, 1971.

Olson, Keith W. *Biography of A Progressive: Franklin K. Lane, 1864–1920*. Westport, Conn.: Greenwood Press, 1979.

Paul, Rodman W. *The Far West and the Great Plains in Transition, 1859–1900*. New York, N.Y.: Harper and Row, 1988.

Peffer, E. Louise. *The Closing of the Public Domain*. Palo Alto, Calif.: Stanford University Press, 1951.

Penick, James, Jr. *Progressive Politics and Conservation*. Chicago: University of Chicago Press, 1969.

Phillips, Clifton J. *Indiana in Transition: The Emergence of an Industrial Commonwealth, 1880–1920*. Indianapolis: Indiana Historical Bureau and Indiana Historical Society, 1968.

Pinchot, Gifford. *Breaking New Ground*. New York: Harcourt, Brace and Company, 1947.

Pisani, Donald J. *From Family Farm to Agribusiness*. Berkeley: University of California Press, 1984.

Pratt, Helen Gay. *Hawaii, Off-Shore Territory*. New York: Charles Scribner's Sons, 1944.

Preston, Richard A., ed. *The Influence of the United States on Canadian*

Development: Eleven Case Studies. No. 40 in series published by Duke University Commonwealth Studies Center. Durham, N.C.: Duke University Press, 1972.

Pringle, Henry F. *Theodore Roosevelt, A Biography*. New York: Harcourt, Brace and Company, 1931.

Revusky, A. *Jews in Palestine*. New York: Vanguard Press, 1936.

Robbins, Roy. *Our Landed Heritage: The Public Domain, 1776–1936*. Princeton: Princeton University Press, 1942.

Roberts, Sir Stephen H. *History of Australian Land Settlement, 1788–1920*. Melbourne: Macmillan Company of Australia, 1924, repr. 1968.

Schmitt, Peter J. *Back to Nature: The Arcadian Myth in Urban America, 1900–1930*. New York: Oxford University Press, 1969.

Shaw, A. G. L. *A Short History of Australia*. New York: Frederick A. Praeger, 1967.

Shaw, A. G. L., and H. D. Nicholson. *Australia in the Twentieth Century*. Melbourne: Angus and Robertson, 1967.

Starr, Kevin. *Inventing the Dream: California through the Progressive Era*. New York: Oxford University Press, 1985.

Stevens, Joseph E. *Hoover Dam: An American Adventure*. Norman: University of Oklahoma Press, 1988.

Steinel, Alvin T., and D. W. Working. *History of Agriculture in Colorado*. Fort Collins, Colo.: State Agricultural College, 1926.

Swain, Donald Christie. *Federal Conservation Policy, 1921–1933*. Berkeley: University of California Press, 1963.

Tennant, Kylie. *Australia: Her Story*. London: Macmillan Company, 1962.

Thornbrough, Emma Lou. *Indiana in the Civil War Era, 1850–1880*. Indianapolis: Indiana Historical Bureau and Indiana Historical Society, 1965.

Webb, Walter Prescott. *The Great Plains*. New York: Ginn and Company, 1931.

Articles

Baker, I. G. "Elwood Mead in Australia." *Aqua* 2, no. 6 (February 1951): 3–11.

Conkin, Paul K. "The Vision of Elwood Mead." *Agriculture History* 34 (April 1960): 88–97.

Connors, Tom. "Closer Settlement Schemes." *The Australian Quarterly* 42, no. 1 (March 1970): 72–85.

Dunbar, Robert G. "The Origins of the Colorado System of Water-Right Control." *The Colorado Magazine* 27 (October 1950): 241–62.

———. "Water Conflicts and Control in Colorado." *Agriculture History* 22 (July 1948): 180–92.

Ganoe, John T. "The Origins of a National Reclamation Policy." *Mississippi Valley Historical Review* 18 (June 1931): 34–52.

Hansen, Anne Carolyn. "The Congressional Career of Senator Francis E. Warren." *Annals of Wyoming* 20 (January 1948): 3–49.

Hess, Ralph. "The Beginnings of Irrigation in the U.S." *Political Economy* 20 (October 1912): 807–28.

Jackson, W. Turrentine. "Administration of Thomas Moonlight, 1887–89." *Annals of Wyoming* 18 (July 1946): 139–62.

Lee, Lawrence B. "The Canadian-American Irrigation Frontier, 1884–1914," *Agricultural History* 40 (October 1965): 271–83.

———. "William E. Smythe and the Irrigation Movement: A Reconsideration. *Pacific Historical Review* 41 (August 1972): 289–311.

Lilly, William, III, and Lewis L. Gould. "The Western Irrigation Movement, 1878–1902: A Reappraisal." *The American West: A Reorientation,* ed. Gene Gressley (Laramie: University of Wyoming Publications 1966), 52–74.

Page, John C. "Memorial to Dr. Elwood Mead, Late Reclamation Commissioner." *The Reclamation Era* 26 (November 1936): 247–50.

Pisani, Donald J. "Enterprise and Equity: A Critique of Western Water Law in the Nineteenth Century." *Western Historical Quarterly* 18, no. 1 (January 1987): 15–37.

———. "Water Law Reform in California, 1900–1913." *Agriculture History* 54 (1980): 295–317.

Reid, Bill G. "Agrarian Opposition to Franklin K. Lane's Proposal for Soldier Settlement, 1918–1921." *Agriculture History* 41 (April 1967): 167–79.

———. "Franklin K. Lane's Idea for Veterans' Colonization, 1918–1921." *Pacific Historical Review* 33 (November 1964): 447–61.

———. "Proposals for Soldier Settlement during World War I." *Mid-America* 46 (July 1964): 172–86.

Smith, Roy J. "The California State Land Settlements at Durham and Delhi." *Hilgardia* 15, no. 5 (October 1943): 399–492.

Sutton, Imre. "Geographical Aspects of Construction Planning: Hoover Dam Revisited." *Journal of the West* 7, no. 3 (July 1968): 301–44.

Swain, Donald C. "The Bureau of Reclamation and the New Deal, 1933–1940." *Pacific Northwest Quarterly* 61, no. 3 (July 1970): 137–46.

Walker, Tacetta. "Wyoming's Fourth Governor—William A. Richards." *Annals of Wyoming* 20 (July 1948): 99–130.

Walter, R. F., and W. H. Code, with the assistance of Frank Adams. "Elwood Mead, M. Am. Soc. C. E." *American Society of Civil Engineers Transactions* 102 (1937): 1611–18.

Wright, D. I. "River Murray—A Continuing Debate." *Journal of the Royal Australian Historical Society* 61, no. 3 (September 1975): 165–84.

Newspapers

Wall Street Journal, September 9, 1991.

Unpublished Materials

Kehlenback, Dorothy, Iowa State University Archivist, to author, February 24, 1970.

Lee, Lawrence B. "Elwood Mead and the Beginnings of National Reclamation." Typescript, article.

Miller, James R. "Pioneer College Presidents." Typescript, Colorado State University, Fort Collins, Colo., 1962.

Peterson, J. T. Typescript biography of Elwood Mead. American Heritage Center, University of Wyoming, n.d.

Wattles, Ruth J. "The Mile High College: A History of Colorado A and M." Typescript, Colorado State University, Fort Collins, Colo., n.d.

Wilbur, Ray Lyman, Jr. "Boulder City: A Survey of Its Legal Background, Its City Plan and Its Administration." Master's thesis, Syracuse University, 1935.

Index